KEY ACCOUNTING PRINCIPLES WORKBOOK

Volume Two, Fourth Edition

Lead Author
Neville Joffe

Contributors and Reviewers

Bharat Aggarwal, BBA, MBA, CMA
Sheridan College

Maria Belanger, CPA, CA
Algonquin College

Ben Carnovale, BBA, MASc
Confederation College

Annette deWeerd, CMA, CGA, MBA
Northern Alberta Institute of Technology

Dave Hummel, CPA, CA
Conestoga College

Laurette Korman, MBA, CMA
Kwantlen Polytechnic University

Chris Leduc, CPA, CA
Cambrian College

Kayla Levesque, CPA, CA
Cambrian College

Sarah Magdalinski, CA, MPACC, BCOMM
Northern Alberta Institute of Technology

Penny Parker, MBA, CPA, CGA
Fanshawe College

Susan Rogers, CPA, CMA
Sheridan College

Ruby So, B. Comm, CA, CGA
Northern Alberta Institute of Technology

AME | Learning

Textbook ISBN: 978-1-926751-31-3
Workbook ISBN: 978-1-926751-32-0

Key Accounting Principles Workbook, Volume 2, Fourth Edition
Author: Neville Joffe
Publisher: AME Learning Inc.
Content Contributors and Developmental Editors:
        Vicki Austin/Kobboon Chotruangprasert
Production Editors: Graeme Gomes/Melody Yousefian
Copy Editor: Nicola Balfour/Lisa McManus
Indexer: Elizabeth Walker
Typesetter: Paragon Prepress Inc.
Vice President and Publishing Manager: Linda Zhang
Cover Design: Sasha Moroz/Bram Wigzell
Online Course Design & Production: AME Multimedia Team

3 4 5 MCRL 19 18 17

This workbook is written to provide accurate information on the covered topics.
It is not meant to take the place of professional advice.

For more information contact:

AME Learning Inc.
410-1220 Sheppard Avenue East
Toronto, ON, Canada M2K 2S5
Phone: 416.479.0200
Toll-free: 1.888.401.3881
E-mail: info@amelearning.com
Visit our website at: www.amelearning.com

Table of Contents

Chapter 1

RECOGNITION AND MEASUREMENT

LEARNING OUTCOMES

❶ Explain the objective and list the key components of the conceptual framework of accounting

❷ Describe the fundamental and enhancing qualitative characteristics of financial information

❸ Explain the underlying assumptions and the concept of cost constraint in financial reporting

❹ List and describe the basic elements of financial statements

❺ List and apply the revenue and expense recognition criteria under IFRS

❻ Describe the three bases of measurement criteria under IFRS

AMEENGAGE™ Access **ameengage.com** for integrated resources including tutorials, practice exercises, the digital textbook and more.

Assessment Questions

AS-1 (❶)

What reporting standards are publicly traded corporations required to follow in Canada?

_____

_____

_____

AS-2 (❶)

Your friend has incorporated a small, private coin laundry business. Which accounting standard would you advise her to use for reporting purposes and why?

_____

_____

_____

_____

AS-3 (❶)

List the key components of the conceptual framework of accounting.

_____

_____

_____

_____

_____

AS-4 (❷)

List and describe the two fundamental qualitative characteristics that IFRS requires in order to provide useful financial information.

_____

_____

_____

_____

_____

AS-5 (❷)

What are the four enhancing qualitative characteristics defined by IFRS?

_____

_____

_____

_____

_____

AS-6 (❷)

Your financial advisor has just informed you that the firm you are considering to purchase shares from reported an exceptionally good net income seven years ago. What characteristic is this information is lacking?

_____

_____

_____

_____

AS-7 (❷)

The bookkeeper of Minco Inc., which is a large multinational company, forgot to record a $25 parking expense, which was incurred on the last day of the company's fiscal year end. The statements were approved and issued to the public. Is this omission material? Explain.

_____

_____

_____

_____

_____

_____

AS-8 (❷)

Information is faithfully represented in the financial statements when which three characteristics are present?

_____

_____

_____

_____

AS-9 (❷)

The financial statements of Borg Ltd. show a loan payable of $200,000 at the end of the year with no notes on repayment terms or interest charged. Which fundamental qualitative characteristic does this information lack?

_____

_____

_____

_____

AS-10 (❷)

What principle ensures completeness of financial information?

_____

_____

_____

_____

AS-11 (❷)

Mike Grump, the CEO of Kaizen Chiefs Inc., instructed the accounting team to defer the recognition of additional revenue earned in the year until the next fiscal year because he has already met his sales targets (which entitle him to receive his bonus). Which fundamental qualitative characteristic will the financial statements lack? Explain.

_____

_____

_____

_____

_____

_____

AS-12 (❷)

The management of Max Co. has decided to measure inventory using FIFO because this method truly represents Max Co.'s movement of inventory in practice, is the most commonly used method in the industry and provides the most reliable information to the end users. Which fundamental qualitative characteristics does this choice help satisfy?

_____

_____

_____

AS-13 (❷)

Financial statements are typically released on an annual basis, with quarterly statements also released by the public corporations. Which principle does periodic reporting satisfy?

_____

_____

_____

AS-14 (❷)

Why is timeliness an important enhancing qualitative characteristic of financial information?

_____

_____

_____

AS-15 (❷)

Clue Inc. has reported $150,000 in revenue in the fiscal year of 2016. A large cash sale worth $80,000 is missing an invoice and related paperwork. Which enhancing qualitative characteristic cannot be met by Clue?

_____

_____

_____

AS-16 (❸)

Marco just opened a Search Engine Optimization business (not incorporated). He continues to use his chequing account to deposit business revenue and uses his personal visa for various business expenses. Explain what underlying assumption he is violating.

_____

_____

_____

_____

AS-17 (❸)

Maltirosa Ltd. is expecting to declare bankruptcy within the next four months and has been experiencing major difficulties in the past year. The recently released financial statements do not disclose the impending bankruptcy. Which underlying assumption is violated in this scenario?

_____

_____

_____

AS-18 (❸)

The various revenue streams of Axinom Ltd., a Canadian corporation that conducts business in Europe, Japan and the United States, have been reported in the functional currencies of the countries in which the revenue was earned. Which underlying assumption is violated in the situation above?

_____

_____

_____

AS-19 (❸)

What is one reason that the AcSB allows private corporations to report financial information under ASPE while requiring public companies to adopt IFRS?

_____

_____

_____

_____

_____

_____

AS-20 (❹)

Define an asset.

_____

_____

_____

AS-21 (❹)

Which financial statement element can be described as a future legal obligation that will require an outflow of resources?

_____

_____

AS-22 (❹)

Explain why an expense is defined as a decrease in equity.

_____

_____

_____

_____

AS-23 (❹)

What is the name of the balance sheet under IFRS? Describe the major differences between the listing orders of the various categories and components under IFRS.

_____

_____

_____

_____

_____

AS-24 (❹)

What is the name of the income statement under IFRS? Describe one major difference from the income statement under ASPE.

_____

_____

_____

AS-25 (❺)

In accrual-based accounting, when does revenue need to be recorded?

_____

_____

AS-26 (❺)

Define the accounting principle of recognition.

_____

_____

_____

AS-27 (❺)

When recognizing an asset on the financial statement, must it be certain that the resource will provide future economic benefit?

_____

_____

_____

_____

AS-28 (❺)

A retailer sold a TV which comes with a three-year warranty. Is the warranty a liability from the perspective of the retailer? Explain why or why not.

_____

_____

_____

_____

_____

AS-29 (❻)

Explain the difference between the completed-contract method and the percentage-of-completion method for revenue recognition. Which method is allowed under IFRS?

_____

_____

_____

_____

_____

_____

_____

AS-30 (◐)

Which process is used to determine the amount at which an item should be recorded on the financial statements? Which bases of measurement are allowed under IFRS?

_____

_____

_____

AS-31 (◐)

What are the advantages and disadvantages of the historical cost base of measurement?

_____

_____

_____

_____

AS-32 (◐)

Explain the concept of fair value measurement. Why is it used by corporations?

_____

_____

_____

AS-33 (◐)

What is the most common measurement base used under IFRS to value liabilities such as bonds?

_____

_____

─────────── **Application Questions Group A** ───────────

AP-1A (❶)

Greg Milgram, the CEO of Vloet Crove Ltd. (VC) was surprised to find a short article in the morning newspaper about Molly Cleverly. She is the firm's administrative assistant, but also volunteers as a board director at a local not-for-profit organization called Save the Finch. At this role, she made significant progress in the preservation of the domestic finch. Greg decided to invite Molly to speak to VC shareholders at the upcoming convention and pulled up a copy of Save the Finch financial statements to review, entertaining the possibility of making a donation to the organization.

Required

a) What type of a financial statement user is Greg Milgram from the perspective of Vloet Crove Ltd. and from Save the Finch?

_____

_____

_____

_____

b) What type of a financial statement user is Molly Cleverly from the perspective of Vloet Crove Ltd. and from Save the Finch?

_____

_____

_____

c) What type of financial statement users are the shareholders of Vloet Crove Ltd. from the perspective of Vloet Crove Ltd. and Save the Finch?

_____

_____

_____

_____

_____

_____

AP-2A (❶)

You incorporated a small apparel company together with your best friend. You each invested $20,000 in the start-up with no external funding. Six months into the enterprise, you both quit your day jobs and are busy working for the new company. The business is immensely successful and generated in excess of $1,000,000 in revenue at the six month mark. Your uncle, an investment banker, believes that it's the perfect time for you to offer the company's shares to the public and become multimillionaires overnight. You and your partner would rather not surrender a stake of your company to the public through initial offering, and would like to develop the company internally, retaining full control and staying away from external investors and the public market.

As the first year anniversary of your corporation approaches, you need to decide what reporting framework you will be using. What would be the best choice for you under these circumstances, ASPE or IFRS?

_____

_____

_____

_____

_____

AP-3A (❷)

For each scenario, indicate which qualitative characteristic from the list was not followed.

- Comparability
- Completeness
- Timeliness

- Understandability
- Neutrality
- Verifiability

Required

a) The management of Vickers Inc., which incurred substantial net loss in fiscal 2016, decides to change its expense policy to a much more aggressive one. It recognizes many of the prepaid expenses this fiscal year to have less expense to record during the next fiscal year, and increase the chances of showing positive net income in 2017.

_____

_____

b) The total depreciation expense of Hernekein Ltd. is $750,000 for fiscal 2016. No depreciation rates or classes of depreciation are provided in the notes to the financial statements.

_____

_____

c) Smaugly Ltd. has changed its inventory valuation technique from FIFO to moving weighted average this year with no substantial change observed in the nature of the inventory or operations of the company. Virtually all of Smaugly's competitors use FIFO. Management justified this move by the fact that the new accountant they hired did not understand FIFO.

_____

_____

d) Jaggernaut Co. provides a prepaid expense card to each of its field employees to compensate them for travelling expenses. At the year-end, once reconciliation was performed, the accountant realized that none of the employees had kept the receipts to support the expenses incurred through the year.

_____

_____

e) Continental Moving Inc. has delayed the release of its financial statements for three months past the due date as it was struggling to complete its truck inventory count. As a result, the statements were released to the public seven months after the statement date.

_____

_____

f) Poet Co. has prepared the notes to the financial statements using Shakesperean English for fiscal 2016. The long-term debt note for instance states the following: "To pay or not to pay, that is the question."

_____

_____

AP-4A (❷)

Jim Billings, the accountant of Calimero Ltd., has begun his day by scanning through the daily assignments list prepared by the department's manager.

Required

For each task, indicate which qualitative characteristic(s) would be violated if Jim followed the instruction.

a) I want you to defer the recognition of the $250,000 in sales made this year to next fiscal year; we already met the sales targets for the year.

_____

_____

b) Can you make the notes to the financial statements really complicated this year? I want the competitors to be confused and scratch their heads when they read our statements. Make sure they won't understand where the figures are coming from.

_____

_____

c) I just came back from Venice and spent about $50,000 on a motel and transportation back and forth from the airport during the one day I was there. Europe is expensive! I don't happen to have any receipts; just record these amounts as a corporate expense.

_____

_____

d) Remember that $200,000 interest-free loan I took from the company a few weeks ago? Make sure to state that it will be repaid next month (although I have no intention of repaying it any time soon).

_____

_____

e) I don't like the amortization method we use; it shows too much depreciation expense. Can you reduce it by half this year? I don't care that the competition uses the previous method; I need to show good profits consistently.

_____

_____

f) I know that we usually prepare financial statements semi-annually but I'm planning to take the company jet for a spin to the Caribbean around the semi-annual submission deadline, so let's defer the semi-annual statements by three months.

_____

_____

AP-5A (❸)

Snobis Ltd. is a privately held manufacturer of high-end parkas. As the company experiences strong growth, the management has decided to undergo a review engagement this year in the hopes of making the financial statements more appealing to potential investors when they take their company public. The auditors identified the following activities.

Required

For each activity the auditors identified, indicate the underlying assumptions and concepts of financial reporting that have been violated. Include any other issues that have to be considered.

a) The company reports under ASPE and wants to continue to report using this framework as the costs of implementing IFRS are considered by management to be beyond the potential benefits this may entail.

_____

_____

b) The management of Snobis occasionally draws out small cash amounts from the corporate bank account to purchase groceries and small household items for themselves.

_____

_____

c) Much of the sales this year were generated from the Japanese market. The sales are recorded in Japanese yen on the income statement but all other items are reported in Canadian dollars.

_____

_____

d) Canada Moose, Snobis' largest competitor, has sued Snobis recently alleging that the company stole its designs. The lawyers indicated that it is quite likely that the lawsuit will be accepted and the company will be forced to declare bankruptcy because it will no longer be allowed to produce any of its products and a large penalty will need to be paid. Management, in the meanwhile, continues to operate as usual. No notes to the financial statements or any changes to the valuation of the company's assets were made.

_____

_____

AP-6A (❸)

Lisa Martok has incorporated her small nail salon in January and decided to ask her friend, a first-year accounting student, for advice on how to keep her books. Her friend has recommended her to adopt IFRS and prepare monthly financial statements. What basic concept does her friend seem to be missing? Explain.

_____

_____

AP-7A (❹)

Milkman Inc. has the following assets as of December 31, 2016.

Trucks	$550,000
Accumulated Depreciation	45,000
Cash	130,000
Accounts Receivable	90,000
Prepaid Insurance	30,000

Required

a) Arrange the items in the liquidity order that is commonly presented on the statement of financial position under IFRS.

_____

_____

_____

_____

b) Arrange the items in the liquidity order that is commonly presented on the balance sheet under ASPE.

_____

_____

_____

_____

_____

AP-8A (❹)

Calypso Ltd. had opening retained earnings of $150,000 on January 1, 2016, had net income of $250,000 and paid dividends of $80,000. Prepare the statement of changes in equity for the company's December 31, 2016 year-end to show the change in retained earnings only.

AP-9A (❺)

Serpico Ltd. has purchased a 25-m crane from Crane Co. for a total of $600,000. The sale was finalized on March 26, 2016 when Serpico provided a clear credit check and paid the first installment of $200,000 with the terms of the sale being FOB destination. The Crane was shipped from London, Ontario to Edmonton, Alberta and arrived on April 1. Crane Co. has a March 31, 2016 year-end. What amount, if any, of the total revenue should be recognized by Crane Co. on the March 31 financial statements? Evaluate the situation against each of the five revenue recognition criteria for sale of goods.

_____

_____

_____

_____

_____

_____

_____

_____

_____

_____

_____

_____

_____

_____

_____

_____

_____

Analysis

Would the timing of recognition be changed if the terms of the sale were FOB shipping instead of destination?

_____

_____

_____

_____

_____

_____

AP-10A (❺)

Avonshire Developments Inc., a publicly traded corporation, was contracted by a local parish to perform massive renovations to the aging church building in Waterloo, Ontario. The renovations were to be conducted in phases over four years starting in 2016. The total contract price agreed upon was $3.5 million. The following costs were incurred by Avonshire over the four years construction took place.

2016	$600,000
2017	$300,000
2018	$900,000
2019	$200,000

The project was completed in 2019, as scheduled, with no amounts outstanding.

Calculate the gross profit of Avonshire for each of the four years using the percentage-of-completion method.

Year	Actual Costs Incurred	Percentage of Completion	Revenue Recognized	Gross Profit
2016				
2017				
2018				
2019				

AP-11A (❻)

Aurora Borealis Ltd. operates a cold storage facility that has 25 huge refrigerators. The company recently purchased a new refrigerator. Aurora paid $400,000 in cash, $250,000 in a note payable and gave the retailer an old refrigerator with an amortized cost of $80,000 and fair value of $100,000 in exchange for the new refrigerator.

Determine the cost of the new refrigerator.

_____

_____

_____

_____

_____

AP-12A (⊙)

Madger Solutions, a manufacturer of micro-processors, has machinery that is used to produce complex electronic components for its products. The company is publicly traded and uses the revaluation model under IFRS to account for the equipment. At year-end, the equipment had a fair market value of $380,000. The amount at which equipment is recorded on the books before revaluation is $400,000 with an accumulated depreciation of $40,000. Prepare a calculation showing the amount of gain or loss to be recorded at the end of this fiscal year under the revaluation model.

_____

_____

_____

_____

_____

Analysis

Identify some drawbacks to using the revaluation method to record the value of non-current assets.

_____

_____

_____

_____

_____

_____

_____

_____

_____

_____

_____

Application Questions Group B

AP-1B (❶)

For each of the individuals, companies or organizations in italics and bold below, determine whether they are an internal or external user in the situation described.

	Mike Jones is a majority shareholder and the CFO of Jeans For Life Inc.
	Crane Inc. is a supplier of replacement parts to Ferroni Ltd., an Italian car manufacturer.
	BRO National Bank is a lender to Creole Ltd.
	Mansfield International Ltd. is a producer of toys, who directly competes with Bolster Ltd for the toy soldiers market share.
	You are a customer of Figley's, a multinational chain of superstores.
	The Canada Revenue Agency is the governmental organization to whom Megaband Ltd. just submitted its annual financial statements and tax return as required by law.
	Chloe Blinick is the director of operations of Astana Corporation.
	Navigana, a global GPS manufacturer, just released its semiannual statements to the *shareholders* and the public.
	Angel Invorssen, an angel investor who is interested in funding HailUs, a promising start-up based in Toronto, is reviewing the financial statements to determine the feasibility of the investment.

AP-2B (❶)

Toronto Chariots F.C. is a relatively new soccer club competing in the top tier of the North American soccer league. Two years ago, the club's shares were offered to the public through an initial public offering on the Toronto Stock Exchange (TSX). While initially successful, the shares price took a hard hit as the club entered into a stretch of bad results. The club management decided to purchase all the shares back and delist the company from the stock market, reversing to a private ownership model. This move was finalized at the beginning of this year. The company can potentially offer the shares to the public again in the future but there is no certainty whether this will take place. Which reporting framework should the Chariots use when preparing their financial statements?

_____

_____

_____

_____

AP-3B (❷)

For each of the scenarios below, indicate which qualitative characteristic was not followed based on the following list

- Comparability
- Completeness
- Timeliness

- Understandability
- Neutrality
- Verifiability

a) While reviewing its documents, Conamco Inc. has discovered that no dividend resolutions were prepared and filed with the legal counsel for the dividends issued last year, yet it appears that dividends were in fact issued to the shareholders.

b) Calipso Ltd., a multinational pharmaceutical corporation, has decided to acquire a majority stake in Neva Inc., its biggest competitor in the generic drug market, for $50 billion. No official press conference was conducted to announce the acquisition until four months after the acquisition has been finalized.

c) The management of Cystico Ltd. ignores the corporate accountant's suggestion to reduce the useful life of the computer equipment and depreciate it over a shorter period, thus taking less depreciation in the current year, as it wants to show a positive bottom line figure to investors.

d) Navara Inc. has decided to add an additional 42-page long note to this year's financial statement, providing the equations used in its asset valuation models, which were developed by 15 mathematicians over the last seven years.

e) Closki Ltd. has been recording its office and administration expenses in an account named "Office & Administrative" on the general ledger. The company replaced its accountant during the year and he recorded all the same expenses in the "Other Expenses" account. The statements were released using the new account.

_____

_____

f) Cordova Moving Ltd. has a corporate jet on the books worth $1 million. The jet recently underwent a major engine re-haul which increased its useful life by three years. No notes concerning the matter have been prepared on the financial statements.

_____

_____

AP-4B (❷)

You have just been hired as a summer intern with Red Brick Limited, a private construction supplies distributor. While reviewing the draft financial statements for fiscal 2016, you have identified the following items.

Required

For each item, indicate which qualitative characteristic is violated.

a) A $250,000 loan was advanced to the corporation by the CFO's father. The loan is interest-free but repayable within one year, yet no such information is disclosed in the notes to the financial statements.

_____

_____

b) Due to the economic downturn, one of Red Brick's biggest customers requested to delay the payment of receivables over and above the normal terms. There are some media reports that the company may go bankrupt soon. Management does not want to write off any receivables this year as this will have a substantial impact on the company's profits.

_____

_____

c) The CFO's father, a successful real estate magnate, provides Red Brick with rental space for its storage and office space and charges rent at fair market rates on a monthly basis. As he is a family member, he does not invoice Red Brick and hasn't been doing so since the firm's inception.

_____

_____

_____

d) The company operates a fleet of leased vehicles for transportation and delivery of supplies. While each lease has a specific, identifiable interest rate, Red Brick uses its own standard 5% interest rate when reporting the interest expense on the leases because it's more convenient.

_____

_____

_____

e) The bank granted Red Brick a loan with accounts receivable used as collateral. Red Brick informed the bank of a potential bad-debt write-off only after receiving the loan.

_____

_____

_____

f) The company initially adopted the IFRS framework, but abandoned it one year later, then adopted IFRS again the following year due to regulatory requirements for a specific contract. The contract is now finished and Red Brick reports under ASPE again this year.

_____

_____

_____

_____

_____

_____

AP-5B (❸)

Linkes Inc. is a publicly traded residential developer of condominiums. You were recently hired as its accountant and found the following while reviewing the financial statements in anticipation of an annual audit.

Required

For each situation, identify the underlying assumptions and concepts of financial reporting that have been violated.

a) Greg Vikas, the majority shareholder and CEO, has funded several corporate construction projects this year using personal funds because of the company's cash shortage.

_____

_____

_____

_____

b) The company is currently engaged in several construction projects in Greece. All of these revenue amounts are reported in euros while the rest of the accounts are reported in Canadian dollars.

_____

_____

_____

_____

c) This year, the company acquired a large parcel of land for development in Barrie, investing the remaining cash it had and borrowing millions from the bank. A major condominium was planned to be erected but further surveying discovered that the land is not suitable for construction. Management is uncertain about the future of the company and whether they can recover. No notes to the financial statements have been prepared and the assets were not revaluated by management.

_____

_____

_____

_____

AP-6B (❸)

Punta Famta Inc. is a large distributor of carbonated drinks operating in North America. The CFO is very detail oriented and when she discovered a $28.00 difference in the year-end cash reconciliation report, she instructed a team of three accountants to find the discrepancy by reviewing the annual cash ledger. The discrepancy was discovered and corrected by the end of the week, with a cumulative 60 hours spent at $75.00 per hour. Explain what basic concept the CFO is missing.

_____

_____

_____

_____

_____

AP-7B (❹)

Tallageda Racing Ltd. has the following assets as of December 31, 2016.

Building	$800,000
Accumulated Depreciation	350,000
Cash	200,000
Accounts receivable	120,000
Interest receivable	14,000
Inventory	65,000

Required

a) Arrange the items in the liquidity order that is commonly presented on the statement of financial position under IFRS.

_____

_____

_____

_____

_____

_____

_____

b) Arrange the items in the liquidity order that is commonly presented on the balance sheet under ASPE.

_____

_____

_____

_____

_____

AP-8B (❹)

On January 1, 2016, Jim Varenik, a sole proprietor, had opening owner's capital of $350,000, invested $45,000 into the business, generated a net income of $70,000 and withdrew $130,000 from the proprietorship's bank account for personal needs. Prepare the statement of owner's in equity for Jim's December 31, 2016 year-end.

AP-9B (⑤)

Yamasaki Customs Ltd., a public corporation with a September 30 year-end, has agreed to re-build and restore a custom motorcycle for Jeff Bezus, a collector of rare vehicles. Yamasaki quoted $20,000 for the job to be completed within one week (the average turnaround for the industry). Jeff agreed and brought the motorcycle to Yamasaki's shop on September 29 and paid $2,500 as a deposit. The work on the motorcycle started on October 1 and was completed on October 3, 2016. Jeff paid the final invoice of $17,500 on October 3, 2016.

What amount, if any, of the total $20,000 in revenue should be recognized by Yamasaki on the September 30, 2016 financial statements? Evaluate the situation against each of the four revenue recognition criteria for sale of services.

AP -10B (❺)

Leonid Glebovski has agreed to pay $50 million for a custom-made yacht ordered from Dream Yacht Ltd., a publicly traded corporation. The yacht was constructed over four years with the following costs incurred by Dream Yacht.

2016	$20,000,000
2017	$6,000,000
2018	$4,000,000
2019	$2,000,000

The project was completed on time and all amounts paid in full.

Calculate the revenue recognized by Dream Yacht in each year using the percentage-of-completion method.

Year	Actual Costs Incurred	Percentage of Completion	Revenue Recognized
2016			
2017			
2018			
2019			

Analysis

Identify some drawbacks to the percentage-of-completion method to recognize revenue.

_____

_____

_____

_____

_____

_____

_____

_____

_____

AP-11B (⑥)

Thompson Deliveries is a moving company with a fleet of 50 trucks. The corporation agreed to purchase a new 2016 model D900 trailer to expand operations to long-distance container hauling. The transaction was finalized with the following terms.

Thompson paid $5,000 cash and issued a note payable for $50,000.
Thompson provided the following three trucks in exchange for the trailer.

> Reno 500 2009 model—Cost $50,000, accumulated depreciation $50,000, fair value $10,000
>
> Congi 3000 2012 model—Cost $40,000, accumulated depreciation $30,000, fair value $20,000
>
> Bonobo L20 2014 model—Cost $20,000, accumulated depreciation $5,000, fair value $15,000

The manufacturer suggested retail price of the D900 is $110,000.

Determine what amount should be recorded in Thompson's books for the purchase.

AP-12B (❻)

Manitoba Telecom is a cellular carrier operating from Winnipeg. The company has wireless signal amplifier installations across the province and uses the revaluation model under IFRS to account for this equipment. In fiscal 2016, it was determined that the fair value of the amplifiers is $9 million. The actual amount currently recorded on the books is as follows.

Amplifiers	$12,000,000
Accumulated Depreciation	3,000,000

Note that $2,000,000 worth of amplifiers were damaged due to a severe storm across the province and will need to be written off this year. The write off has not yet been recorded; however, the impairment is already factored in the fair value of the amplifiers. Prepare a calculation showing the amount of gain or loss to be recorded at the end of this fiscal year under the revaluation model.

Case Study

CS-1 (❹ ❺)

Pampersky Ltd. is a multinational, publicly traded security software developer with a July 31 year-end. Pampersky specializes in the development of antiviruses but also has a large market share in the corporate security and business IT security solutions. Pampersky is a rapidly growing company and launched its North American operations two years ago, with strong revenue and net income figures reported in the first two years. Pampersky has hired your firm to assist with its reporting and financial statements preparation this year. Greg, the corporate accountant, has provided you with a list of issues, requesting assistance with the treatment of the following transactions.

Required

a) Pampersky entered into a three-year contract with a major investment bank to re-haul its existing security software. The contract was signed in 2014 with Pampersky scheduled to receive $16 million in each of the three years the contract is performed. The 2014 cost was $12 million, the 2015 cost was $10 million and the 2016 cost was $8 million. Greg indicated that revenue was recognized equally over the three years of the contract and asked you to help him recalculate the revenue to be recorded under the percentage-of-completion method.

Year	Actual Costs Incurred	Percentage of Completion	Revenue Recognized
2014			
2015			
2016			

b) Pampersky's antivirus software is extremely successful and is sold exclusively online. The client pays on the spot, using PayPal or other electronic methods, and is allowed to download one copy of the software, which is installed on the computer and activated using a unique code. There is a 30-day money back return policy during which the client can change his mind and return the product for a full refund. Based on the last two year's data, about 5% of the clients utilize the return policy and get their money back. This amount is recorded as contra revenue on the financial statements. Greg indicated that the company recognizes 100% of the revenue when the software is sold (i.e. when the client confirms payment via PayPal). Greg asked you to confirm that the revenue recognition practice is correct.

c) A large project for the installation of a server in a manufacturing facility with a cost of $300,000 and revenue of $500,000 was completed on July 31, 2016. The full payment of $500,000 for the project was received on July 31, 2016. Half the costs were paid in July and the other half were paid in August. The accountant recorded the expense only in August 2016 when the amount was paid. Management approved this move as their bonuses are based on a percentage of net income. Greg is unsure if anything is wrong with this transaction.

_____

_____

_____

_____

_____

_____

_____

d) The company has about $150,000 worth of old software on its books classified as inventory with a cost of $150 per package. This software is three years old and is no longer compatible with new operating systems. Management insists that this software can be sold for at least $140 each but the last time one was sold was last year for $100. The inventory continues to show on the books at $150,000 and Greg indicated that management does not wish to make any changes. He himself is unsure what recognition criteria under IFRS may be violated in this case.

_____

_____

_____

_____

_____

_____

_____

_____

e) The retained earnings of the corporation on August 1, 2015 were $850,000. Net income for fiscal 2016 was $650,000 and dividends totaling $200,000 were paid to common shareholders. Prepare the statement of changes in equity for the year ended July 31, 2016 to report the change in retained earnings only.

f) Greg has learned of a $300,000 grant the company can apply for through the Canadian government to help with business development. There is a long application process, which has not been started. This amount has been recorded as a grant receivable on the statement of financial position of the corporation. Greg is unsure exactly how the grant should be recorded.

_____

_____

_____

_____

_____

_____

_____

_____

_____

_____

_____

Notes

Chapter 2

ACCOUNTING FOR RECEIVABLES

LEARNING OUTCOMES

❶ Explain the importance of accounts receivable

❷ Account for bad debt using the allowance method

❸ Estimate bad debt using income statement and balance sheet approaches

❹ Utilize reports, including the accounts receivable subledger, to manage accounts receivable information

❺ Calculate financial ratios pertaining to accounts receivable

❻ Apply controls relating to accounts receivable

❼ Record promissory notes and notes receivable

❽ Apply ethics relating to accounts receivable and notes receivable

AMEENGAGE *Access **ameengage.com** for integrated resources including tutorials, practice exercises, the digital textbook and more.*

Assessment Questions

AS-1 (❶)

Define accounts receivable.

_____

_____

_____

_____

_____

AS-2 (❶)

Describe the presentation of accounts receivable on the balance sheet.

_____

_____

_____

_____

_____

AS-3 (❹)

How can the subsidiary ledger assist in managing a company's accounts receivable?

_____

_____

_____

_____

_____

_____

AS-4 (❹)

Explain the relationship between the accounts receivable control account and individual customer accounts in the accounts receivable subledger.

_____

_____

_____

_____

_____

_____

AS-5 (❶ ❼)

What is the difference between accounts receivable and notes receivable?

_____

_____

_____

_____

_____

_____

AS-6 (❷)

Explain the nature and purpose of the account called allowance for doubtful accounts.

_____

_____

_____

_____

_____

AS-7 (❸)

Name two different approaches for estimating bad debt expense.

_____

_____

_____

_____

_____

AS-8 (❺)

Name two ratios used to assess accounts receivable, and state the formulas used to calculate the ratios.

_____

_____

_____

_____

_____

AS-9 (❸)

What would cause the AFDA account to have a debit balance?

_____

_____

_____

_____

AS-10 (❼)

What is a dishonoured note? What happens to the balance of notes receivable once the note is dishonoured?

_____

_____

_____

_____

_____

AS-11 (❸)

Which method is best for estimating bad debt: the income statement method or the balance sheet method?

_____

_____

_____

_____

AS-12 (❶)

What are the advantages and disadvantages to a company that sells on credit?

_____

_____

_____

_____

AS-13 (❸)

What pitfalls exist for a company that uses the income statement method for recording bad debt expense?

_____

_____

_____

_____

_____

AS-14 (❺)

How do you interpret the DSO number? The ART ratio?

_____

_____

_____

_____

_____

AS-15 (❹)

Give two examples of accounting reports that can be generated involving accounts receivable.

_____

_____

_____

_____

_____

_____

AS-16 (❻)

What internal controls are important for accounts receivable? Is there any one control that is absolutely necessary?

_____

_____

_____

_____

_____

_____

_____

AS-17 (❽)

What ethical problems are related to accounts receivable? Can they be avoided?

_____

_____

_____

_____

_____

_____

AS-18 (❽)

Suppose a company is in the middle of preparing its financial statements for the fiscal year, and finds out that its net income figure falls a little bit short of Wall Street earnings forecasts. How would management's desire to beat analysts' forecasts potentially influence the estimated amount of bad debt expense?

_____

_____

_____

_____

_____

Application Questions Group A

AP-1A (❷)

On December 31, 2016, your company decides that an allowance for doubtful accounts is required in the amount of $6,000. There is a zero balance in the account. Prepare the journal entry to set up the required allowance.

Date	Account Title and Explanation	Debit	Credit

AP-2A (❷)

Your company decides that an allowance for doubtful accounts is required in the amount of $6,000. There is a $4,000 credit balance in the account. Prepare the journal entry to set up the required allowance on December 31, 2016.

Date	Account Title and Explanation	Debit	Credit

AP-3A (❸)

Your company uses the income statement approach for estimating bad debt. For the year ending December 31, 2016, credit sales amounted to $1 million. The estimated bad debt is 0.5% of credit sales. Prepare the journal entry to record bad debt expense for the year.

Date	Account Title and Explanation	Debit	Credit

AP-4A (❷)

On July 31, 2016, Alou Company's accounts receivable ledger showed an ending balance of $50,000. The company estimates that $2,500 of accounts receivable will become uncollectible. Prepare a journal entry to record estimation of bad debt.

Date	Account Title and Explanation	Debit	Credit

AP-5A (❷ ❸)

D&D Company uses the allowance method to account for uncollectible receivables. During 2016, the company made total credit sales of $1,370,000, of which $328,000 was currently owed by customers at year-end. According to the company's historical sales, 2.5% of total credit sales will be uncollected. D&D Company uses an income statement approach to estimate the amount of uncollectible receivables. The company's year-end is December 31. Prepare the journal entry to account for the amount deemed uncollectible.

Date	Account Title and Explanation	Debit	Credit

AP-6A (❷ ❸)

The Green Earth Company uses the allowance method to account for uncollectible receivables. The company uses the income statement approach for estimating uncollectible receivables. During the fiscal year 2016, the company had credit sales of $2,300,000. It estimates that 1.5% of these sales will be uncollectible. Green Earth Company has a December 31 year-end. Prepare the journal entry to record the uncollectible receivables on December 31, 2016.

Date	Account Title and Explanation	Debit	Credit

AP-7A (❷)

On June 15, 2016, you discover that your customer, Tyrone Huntzinger, has gone bankrupt. He owes you $1,000.

Required

a) Prepare the appropriate journal entry to write off bad debt assuming AFDA has already been estimated and recorded in the past.

Date	Account Title and Explanation	Debit	Credit

b) Assuming that Tyrone Huntzinger's situation changed and he paid you in full on August 20, 2016. Prepare the journal entries to record this transaction.

Date	Account Title and Explanation	Debit	Credit

AP-8A (❷)

A customer's account in the amount of $2,000 was previously written off. Amazingly, on December 31, 2016, you receive a check in the mail from the customer with a letter of apology for not paying sooner (the account is two years old). Prepare the journal entries by using the allowance method.

Date	Account Title and Explanation	Debit	Credit

AP-9A (❷ ❸)

During 2016, Jaime Company made total credit sales of $500,000, of which $25,000 was owed by customers at year-end. On the basis of historical sales, 1% of sales will be uncollectible. Jaime Company uses the allowance method to account for uncollectible receivables, and uses an income statement approach to estimate the amount of receivables that will not be collected.

Required

a) Prepare the journal entry on December 31, 2016 to account for the amount deemed uncollectible.

Date	Account Title and Explanation	Debit	Credit

b) On January 20, 2017, Mrs. L. Green, who owes the company $500, informs Jaime Corporation that she will be unable to pay the amount. Prepare the necessary journal entry.

Date	Account Title and Explanation	Debit	Credit

c) On February 14, 2017, Mrs. L. Green wins a lottery and decides to repay the full amount owing to Jaime Corporation. Prepare the necessary journal entries.

Date	Account Title and Explanation	Debit	Credit

AP-10A (❸)

The 2015 and 2016 sales and accounts receivable information for Velcary Company are shown below.

At the beginning of 2015, the AFDA account had a $0 balance. During 2015, sales for the year totalled $1,200,000 with 60% on credit. At December 31 year-end, accounts receivable had a debit balance of $55,000. Management estimated that 0.5% of all credit sales would be uncollectible. The company wrote off $3,100 worth of accounts receivable at the end of the year.

During 2016, sales totalled $1,630,000 with 60% on credit. On December 31, 2016, accounts receivable has a debit balance of $76,000. During the year, the company wrote off a number of accounts receivable, leaving the allowance for doubtful accounts with a debit balance of $4,500. The estimate for bad debt expense for the year has not been determined or recorded. After reviewing the write-offs, the company decided that the estimated percentage for AFDA should be increased from 0.5% to 0.75%.

Required

a) Prepare the journal entry to record the bad debt expense for 2016.

Date	Account Title and Explanation	Debit	Credit

b) Prepare a T-account for the allowance for doubtful accounts and enter all related transactions for year 2015 and 2016.

c)   What are the net accounts receivable at the end of 2016?

_____

_____

_____

_____

AP-11A (❷ ❸)

The following chart is prepared by the accountant of Happy Shoes. The percentages are based on historical performance.

Aging Category	Bad Debt %	Balance
30 days	1%	$80,000
31–60 days	3%	40,000
More than 60 days	5%	20,000
Total		$140,000

Happy Shoes uses the balance sheet approach to estimate uncollectible receivables.

Required

a)   Calculate the company's bad debt.

Aging Category	Bad Debt %	Balance	Estimated Bad Debt

b)   Assume that allowance for doubtful accounts has a credit balance of $1,000. Calculate the amount of bad debt expense the company will record.

_____

_____

_____

_____

_____

_____

AP-12A (❷ ❸)

Your company uses the balance sheet approach to estimate bad debt. Details of the accounts receivable balances owing on December 31, 2016 are shown below.

Aging Category	Bad debt %	Balance
Under 30 days	1%	$90,000
31–60 days	20%	90,000
More than 60 days	50%	30,000
Total		$210,000

Required

a) Calculate the required allowance.

Aging Category	Bad debt %)	Balance	Required Allowance
Under 30 days	1%	$90,000	
31–60 days	20%	90,000	
More than 60 days	50%	30,000	
Total		$210,000	

b) Write the journal entry to record bad debt expense for the year, assuming that the allowance account has a $20,000 credit balance.

Date	Account Title and Explanation	Debit	Credit

AP-13A (❷ ❸)

The following chart was prepared by the accountant of Happy Shoes. The percentages are based on historical performance. Happy Shoes uses the balance sheet approach to estimate uncollectible receivables.

Required

a) Calculate the company's bad debt.

Aging Category	Bad Debt %	Balance	Estimated Bad Debt
30 days	2%	$76,000	
31–60 days	3.5%	45,000	
More than 60 days	10%	25,000	
Total		$146,000	

b) Assume that allowance for doubtful accounts has a debit balance of $1,100. Calculate the amount of bad debt expense the company will record.

AP-14A (❷ ❸)

Whitney Fabricators uses the balance sheet approach to estimate uncollectible receivables. The following is the aging of receivables on December 31, 2016.

Aging category	Bad Debt %	Balance
Under 30 days	2%	$175,000
31–60 days	4%	40,000
61–90 days	10%	10,000
More than 90 days	60%	3,000
Total		$228,000

Required

a) Calculate the required allowance for doubtful accounts.

Aging category	Bad Debt %	Balance	Allowance for Doubtful Accounts

b) Prepare the journal entry on December 31, 2016 to record bad debt expense assuming the allowance account has a $3,700 credit balance.

Date	Account Title and Explanation	Debit	Credit

c) Prepare the journal entry on December 31, 2016 to record bad debt expense assuming the allowance account has a $10,000 credit balance.

Date	Account Title and Explanation	Debit	Credit

d) Prepare the journal entry to record bad debt expense assuming the allowance account has a $2,000 debit balance.

Date	Account Title and Explanation	Debit	Credit

AP-15A (❺)

Wechsler Company has a net accounts receivable opening balance of $250,000 and ending balance of $300,000. The total sales amount for the year is $1,700,000, of which 80% are on credit. Normal credit terms are 30 days. Calculate the day sales outstanding and the accounts receivable turnover. Comment on the calculated ratios.

AP-16A (❺)

The following information relevant to accounts receivable is presented for Dommar Company (in thousands of dollars).

	2016	2015	2014
Accounts Receivable	$319	$422	$501
Allowance for Doubtful Accounts	19	18	20
Net Credit Sales	$4,377	$3,598	$2,937

Required

a) Calculate the accounts receivable turnover ratio for the years 2015 and 2016.

b) Calculate the day sales outstanding for the years 2015 and 2016.

_____

_____

_____

_____

_____

c) At the 2015 year-end, Dommar Company agreed to sell some of its accounts receivable with a fee paid to the purchaser. Why do you think a company would pay a fee to sell its accounts receivable?

_____

_____

_____

_____

_____

_____

d) Dommar Company sold the accounts receivable on a limited recourse basis. Research and define the meaning of selling on a limited recourse basis.

_____

_____

_____

_____

_____

_____

AP-17A (❼)

Lakisha Ogata operates a proprietorship selling machinery. Because of the high value of the machinery sold, Lakisha often requires customers to sign a note. Lakisha originally sold a Gadget machine to Neil Marcin for $10,000 on November 14, 2016. The sale was initially recorded as an account receivable, but now Lakisha decides to ask Neil to sign a note. On December 1, 2016, Neil signs a one-year note to be paid on maturity, plus 5% interest. Lakisha's company has a year-end of April 30. Prepare the journal entries to reflect the transactions related to the receivable and note.

Date	Account Title and Explanation	Debit	Credit

AP-18A (❼)

On January 1, 2016, Beta Company determined that it would not be able to pay the accounts receivable that was owed to Star Company. Beta Company believed that it would have sufficient cash one year later, therefore signed a one-year notes receivable for the $10,000 that was owed. The annual interest rate is 9%, payable on July 1 and January 1. Star Company has a year-end of June 30. On January 1, 2017, Beta Company dishonoured the note because it went bankrupt. Star Company assessed that the debt will never be collected and decided to immediately write off the note.

Required

a) Record journal entries for Star Company when the note is signed.

Date	Account Title and Explanation	Debit	Credit

b) Prepare journal entries for the year-end adjustment.

Date	Account Title and Explanation	Debit	Credit

c) Prepare journal entries for the receipt of the first interest payment.

Date	Account Title and Explanation	Debit	Credit

d) Prepare journal entries to write off Beta Company's note on January 1, 2017.

Date	Account Title and Explanation	Debit	Credit

AP-19A (❼)

On February 1, 2016, the Success Company accepted a six-month note receivable as an extension of time for a balance of $15,000 owing from Summit Company. The note has an annual interest rate of 7%. Success Company has a June 30 year-end.

Required

Prepare the following journal entries for Success Company.

a) Prepare the journal entry on February 1, 2016.

Date	Account Title and Explanation	Debit	Credit

b) Prepare the journal entry for the year-end adjustment, if required.

Date	Account Title and Explanation	Debit	Credit

c) Summit Company honoured the note. Record the entry upon payment.

Date	Account Title and Explanation	Debit	Credit

AP-20A (❼)

On January 1, 2016, Ashley Manufacturing sold equipment to Henry Company for $200,000 with a cost of $140,000. Henry Company signed a nine-month note for the purchase. The note is due on September 30, 2016 with an annual interest rate of 9%. Ashley Manufacturing has an April 30 year-end and uses a perpetual inventory system. On September 30, Henry Company dishonored the note due to insolvency. Ashley believes that Henry will eventually pay when things get better.

Required

Prepare the following journal entries for Ashley Manufacturing.

a) Prepare journal to record the sale of the equipment.

Date	Account Title and Explanation	Debit	Credit

b) Prepare the journal entry for the year-end adjustment, if required.

Date	Account Title and Explanation	Debit	Credit

c) Prepare the journal entry to record the dishonored note by Henry Company on September 30, 2016.

Date	Account Title and Explanation	Debit	Credit

d) On April 30, 2017 Ashley decided to write off the amount outstanding from Henry Company. Prepare the journal entry to record the transaction.

Date	Account Title and Explanation	Debit	Credit

—————————— **Application Questions Group B** ——————————

AP-1B(❷)

On December 31, 2016, Mann Company's accounts receivable ledger showed an ending balance of $40,000. The company estimates that $2,000 of accounts receivable will become uncollectible. Prepare a journal entry to record the estimation of bad debt.

Date	Account Title and Explanation	Debit	Credit

AP-2B (❷)

On December 31, 2016, your company decides that an allowance for doubtful accounts is required in the amount of $6,000. There is a $1,000 debit balance in the account. Prepare the journal entry to set up the required allowance.

Date	Account Title and Explanation	Debit	Credit

AP-3B (❷ ❸)

B&B Company uses the allowance method to account for uncollectible receivables. During 2016, the company made total credit sales of $1,250,000, of which $300,000 was owed by customers at year-end. According to the company's historical sales, 1.5% of the amount will be uncollected. B&B Company uses an income statement approach to estimate the amount of uncollectible receivables. The company's year-end is December 31. Prepare the journal entry to account for the amount deemed uncollectible.

Date	Account Title and Explanation	Debit	Credit

AP-4B (❷)

After analyzing the current accounts receivable, your company decides that the allowance for doubtful accounts should have an ending normal balance of $5,870. There is a $850 credit balance in the account. Prepare the journal entry to set up the required allowance.

Date	Account Title and Explanation	Debit	Credit

AP-5B (❷ ❸)

The Mayflower company uses the allowance method to account for uncollectible receivables. During 2016, the company had total sales of $750,000, all on credit. The company uses the income statement approach to estimate uncollectible receivables. Historically, the company estimates that 1% of credit sales will be uncollectible. Mayflower Company has a December 31 year-end. Prepare the journal entry to record the uncollectible receivables on December 31, 2016.

Date	Account Title and Explanation	Debit	Credit

AP-6B (❷ ❸)

Johnson Company uses the allowance method to account for uncollectible receivables. During 2016, the company had total sales of $2,500,000. Of this total, $300,000 was cash sales. On December 31, 2016 the company had an accounts receivable balance of $165,000 and a credit balance in allowance for doubtful accounts of $7,000. Johnson Company has a December 31 year-end.

Required

a) Assume the company uses the income statement approach to estimate uncollectible receivables. Historically the company estimates 0.5% of credit sales will be uncollectible. Prepare the journal entry to record bad debt expense on December 31, 2016.

Date	Account Title and Explanation	Debit	Credit

b) Assume the company uses the balance sheet approach and estimates uncollectible receivables to be 7.5% of accounts receivable. Prepare the journal entry to record bad debt expense on December 31, 2016.

Date	Account Title and Explanation	Debit	Credit

c) Assume the AFDA has a debit balance of $2,000 on December 31, 2016. Using the balance sheet approach and estimating that 7.5% of receivables will be uncollectable, prepare the journal entry to record the bad debt expense on December 31, 2016.

Date	Account Title and Explanation	Debit	Credit

AP-7B (❷)

Jane Lee is the owner of a small consulting firm called Lee Solutions. On April 14, 2016, Lee Solutions' accounts receivable account balance was $10,000. A week later, it was discovered that Mr. Joe Black, who owed the firm $1,500, would not be able to make the payment.

Required

a) Prepare a journal entry to write off the amount deemed uncollectible.

Date	Account Title and Explanation	Debit	Credit

b) On May 26, 2016, Mr. Joe Black was able to repay 50% of the amount he owed, which had been previously written off. Prepare the journal entries required to record this transaction.

Date	Account Title and Explanation	Debit	Credit

AP-8B (❷)

On February 8, 2016, you discover that your customer, Gerome Linger, has gone bankrupt. He owes you $910. Prepare the appropriate journal entry to write off bad debt assuming AFDA has already been estimated and recorded in the past.

Date	Account Title and Explanation	Debit	Credit

AP-9B (❷ ❸)

In 2016, Upper Machine Sales Company sold equipment on credit in the amount of $950,000. Total cash collections during the year were $820,000. The company determined that $7,000 of accounts receivable would not be collected and wrote them off. At the end of 2016, management decided to increase its allowance percentage to 1% of credit sales from 0.5% last year because of the amount of accounts receivable that proved to be uncollectible during the year. At the end of 2015, the company had $135,000 in accounts receivable and a credit balance of $6,000 in allowance for doubtful accounts. Assume the company has a year-end of December 31.

Required

a) Prepare the necessary journal entries to record all 2016 transactions including sales, collection, the write-off and the new allowance amount. Disregard the dates when recording the transactions.

Date	Account Title and Explanation	Debit	Credit

b) Show the amount of net accounts receivable on the balance sheet as at December 31, 2016.

_____

_____

_____

_____

AP-10B (❷ ❸)

Dalton Company has the following unadjusted balances on December 31, 2016. All amounts shown are in their normal balance.

Accounts receivable	$425,750
Allowance for doubtful accounts	25,000
Sales (10% of sales are cash sales)	950,000
Sales discounts	15,000

Required

a) Dalton estimates that 1.5% of net credit sales will be uncollectible. Prepare the journal entry to record the uncollectible receivables on December 31, 2016.

Date	Account Title and Explanation	Debit	Credit

b) Prepare the balance sheet presentation of accounts receivable on December 31, 2016.

_____

_____

_____

AP-11B (❷ ❸)

Fishy uses the balance sheet approach to estimate uncollectible receivables. Use the following table to determine the amount of bad debt expense, and prepare the journal entry on June 30, 2016 to record the bad debt expense. The allowance account has a zero balance.

Aging Category	Bad Debt %	Balance
30 days	2%	$25,000
31–60 days	3%	10,000
More than 60 days	4%	2,000
Total		$37,000

Aging Category	Bad Debt %	Balance	Estimated Bad Debt
30 days	2%	$25,000	
31–60 days	3%	10,000	
More than 60 days	4%	2,000	
Total		$37,000	

Date	Account Title and Explanation	Debit	Credit

AP-12B (❷ ❸)

Nortelle Canada operates in an industry that has a high rate of bad debt. Before the year-end adjustments, Nortelle Canada's accounts receivable has a debit balance of $536,000 and the allowance for doubtful accounts had a credit balance of $20,000. The December 31, 2016 year-end balance reported on the balance sheet for the allowance for doubtful accounts is based on the aging schedule shown below.

Aging Category	Bad Debt %	Balance
Less than 16 days	2%	$300,000
16–30 days	3%	100,000
31–45 days	5%	75,000
46–60 days	10%	32,000
61–75 days	20%	18,000
More than 75 days	40%	11,000

Required

a) What is the balance for the allowance for doubtful accounts at year-end?

Aging Category	Bad Debt %	Balance	Estimated Amount of Bad Debt
Less than 16 days	2%	$300,000	
16–30 days	3%	100,000	
31–45 days	5%	75,000	
46–60 days	10%	32,000	
61–75 days	20%	18,000	
More than 75 days	40%	11,000	

b) Prepare the journal entry to record bad debt expense for the year.

Date	Account Title and Explanation	Debit	Credit

AP-13B (❷ ❸)

Williams Canada operates in an industry that has a high rate of bad debts. Before the year-end adjustments on April 30, Williams Canada's accounts receivable has a debit balance of $485,000 and the allowance for doubtful accounts has a credit balance of $15,700. The year-end balance reported on the balance sheet for the allowance for doubtful accounts is based on the aging schedule shown below.

Required

a) Fill in the table to calculate the balance for the allowance for doubtful accounts.

Aging Category	Bad Debt %	Balance	Estimated Bad Debt
Less than 16 days	2%	$270,000	
16–30 days	4%	$84,000	
31–45 days	7%	$71,000	
46–60 days	12%	$30,000	
61–75 days	21%	$17,000	
More than 75 days	44%	$13,000	
Total		$485,000	

b) Prepare the journal entry to record bad debt expense for the year.

Date	Account Title and Explanation	Debit	Credit

AP-14B (❷)

On January 1, 2016, Jay Company's allowance for doubtful accounts had a credit balance of $30,000. During 2016, Jay charged $64,000 to bad debt expense, and wrote off $46,000 of uncollectible accounts receivable. What is the balance of allowance for doubtful accounts on December 31, 2016?

AP-15B (❺)

A company's relevant accounts receivable information for years 2015 and 2016 is provided below.

	2016	2015
Average Net Accounts Receivable	$1,486,739	$1,769,032
Net Credit Sales	23,075,635	22,107,539

Required

a) Calculate the accounts receivable turnover ratio for 2015 and 2016.

b) Calculate the days sales outstanding for 2015 and 2016.

_____

_____

_____

_____

c) Compare and discuss the results from parts a) and b).

_____

_____

_____

_____

AP-16B (❺)

The following information is taken from the records of Hanlan Corporation. Normal credit terms are 30 days.

	2017	2016	2015
Net credit sales	$250,000	$200,000	$190,000
Account receivable	17,500	24,000	32,300
Allowance for doubtful accounts	1,050	960	1,292

Required

a) Calculate the accounts receivable turnover ratio for 2016 and 2017.

_____

_____

_____

_____

b) Calculate the days sales outstanding for the years 2016 and 2017.

_____

_____

_____

c) Comment on the accounts receivable ratios calculated from 2016 and 2017.

_____

_____

_____

_____

AP-17B (❼)

On May 1, 2016, People's Networks sold computer networking supplies to American Autos for $36,000. The cost of the supplies is $15,000. Instead of paying immediately, American Autos signed a note receivable with 11% annual interest, payable in eight months. People's Networks has a year-end of October 31.

Required

a) Record the journal entry when the sale is made; assume People's Networks uses the perpetual inventory system.

Date	Account Title and Explanation	Debit	Credit

b) Prepare the journal entry for the year-end adjustment.

Date	Account Title and Explanation	Debit	Credit

c) Prepare the journal entry for receipt of payment from American Autos on January 1, 2017.

Date	Account Title and Explanation	Debit	Credit

d) What items would be included on the balance sheet and income statement of People's Networks as at October 31, 2016 with respect to this note?

_____

_____

_____

_____

_____

_____

_____

_____

_____

_____

_____

_____

_____

_____

_____

_____

AP-18B (❼)

On January 1, 2016, Delta Company determined that it would not be able to pay the accounts receivable that was owed to Star Company. Delta Company was confident that it would have sufficient cash one year later, therefore signed a one-year notes receivable for the $16,100 that was owed. The annual interest rate is 10%, payable on July 1 and January 1. Star Company has a year-end of June 30.

Required

a) Record the journal entry for Star Company when the note is signed.

Date	Account Title and Explanation	Debit	Credit

b) Prepare the journal entry for the year-end adjustment.

Date	Account Title and Explanation	Debit	Credit

c) Prepare the journal entry for the receipt of first interest payment.

Date	Account Title and Explanation	Debit	Credit

d) Prepare the journal entries for receipt of payment from Delta Company on January 1, 2017.

Date	Account Title and Explanation	Debit	Credit

AP-19B (❼)

On March 1, 2016 Asper Company accepted a $100,000, six-month note from Arctic Company as a time extension on a past-due amount in accounts receivable. The note has an interest rate of 5%.

Required

a) Prepare the journal entry for Asper Company on March 1, 2016.

Date	Account Title and Explanation	Debit	Credit

b) Prepare the journal entry for Asper Company to record the payment of the note in full with interest on August 31, 2016.

Date	Account Title and Explanation	Debit	Credit

AP-20B (❼)

On September 1, 2016, The Highlander Truck Company sold two heavy duty trucks to Zebra Corporation for $160,000. Highlander's cost for the trucks was $135,000. Zebra Corporation signed a seven- month note for the purchase. The note is due on April 1, 2017 with an annual interest rate of 6%. The Highlander Truck Company has a December 31 year-end and uses a perpetual inventory system. On April 1, 2017, Zebra dishonoured the note because the company was going through a tough period and could not afford to pay the balanced owed. The Highlander Truck Company believes that Zebra Corporation will eventually make the payment when the economy improves.

Required

a) Prepare the journal entry to record the sale.

Date	Account Title and Explanation	Debit	Credit

b) Prepare the journal entry for the year-end adjustment, if required.

Date	Account Title and Explanation	Debit	Credit

c) Prepare the journal entry to record the dishonoured note by Zebra Corporation on April 1, 2017.

Date	Account Title and Explanation	Debit	Credit

Case Study

CS-1 (❶ ❸ ❺ ❻)

Softbed Hotel (Softbed) owns and manages a large hotel on the east coast of Canada. The hotel is close to a few popular tourist attractions, and is usually fully booked in the summer. Business is relatively slower in other seasons, when the company gains most of its revenues from business clients organizing events such as trade shows and conferences.

The hotel has established a credit policy. For individual guests, Softbed requires a cash deposit or credit card up front. For large groups of guests and corporate clients, Softbed extends credit selectively, based on the amount of revenue they will generate for the hotel and on their credit information obtained from a reliable independent source. For the clients that Softbed decides to extend its credit to, the credit term is n/30.

Detailed examination of the accounts receivable aging report reveals that because Softbed completes credit checks before extending its credit, there are only rare cases where customers are unable to pay. However, bill dispute is the cause of most long outstanding accounts receivable balances. The billing process is complicated because guests have multiple purchase points (their rooms, restaurants, business centre, spa and souvenir shop). Hotel guests can buy products and services from any of the purchase points and ask for the costs to be billed to their rooms. Sometimes billing mistakes arise due to wrong room numbers being recorded, or the purchase information for each customer not being compiled properly from different purchase points. Also, customers often make last-minute changes to their room arrangements or other arrangements from what they booked prior to their arrival. These changes are recorded manually before being transferred to Softbed's centralized accounts receivable department. Sometimes these changes are improperly recorded or transferred, resulting in incorrect invoices being billed to customers. Once customers dispute their bills, the hotel starts an investigation to validate the customers' claims. The investigation involves checking internal records, and asking various hotel staff about what actually happened with a particular customer. Unfortunately, usually by the time the investigation gets started, the hotel staff has forgotten about what had happened, as they're too busy focusing on the current events at the hotel. The customers usually refuse to pay, or pay only partially, until the disputes involving their bills are resolved, resulting in long outstanding accounts receivable.

Required

a) To account for bad debt, Softbed estimates that 2% of its gross accounts receivable balance will become uncollectible. Use the information provided in the table below to calculate allowance for doubtful accounts balances for 2014 to 2016, and the days sales outstanding and accounts receivable turnover for the years 2015 and 2016. Compare the results of ratio calculations and comment on whether the company's performance has improved or weakened.

	2016	2015	2014
Net Credit Sales	$4,500,000	$4,200,000	$4,000,000
Gross Accounts Receivable	490,000	400,000	770,000
Allowance for Doubtful Accounts			
Days Sales Outstanding			
Accounts Receivable Turnover			

b) What are other methods that Softbed can use to estimate its bad debt? Which method do you think would be most suitable for Softbed?

c) Following Softbed's seasonal business fluctuations, should the company adopt a seasonal credit policy? In other words, should Softbed Hotel use different credit policies for different seasons? Explain.

_____

_____

_____

_____

_____

_____

_____

_____

d) Analyze and identify strengths and weaknesses of Softbed's accounts receivable controls.

_____

_____

_____

_____

_____

_____

_____

_____

_____

_____

_____

Critical Thinking

CT-1 (① ② ③ ④ ⑤ ⑥ ⑧)

You are the Chief Financial Officer for Stanton Feery and Company. Mr. Stanton's friend, Shad Baxtor, is starting up a new company, and needs some advice on accounts receivable and bad debt accounting practices. Mr. Stanton has asked you to meet with Mr. Baxtor and answer a few questions. He hands you a list of things that Shad Baxtor wants clarified.

Required

Answer the following questions for Shad Baxtor.

a) What are accounts receivable?

_____

_____

_____

_____

_____

b) What are bad debts?

_____

_____

_____

_____

_____

_____

_____

_____

c) When are amounts considered bad debt?

_____

_____

_____

_____

d) How is bad debt estimated?

_____

_____

_____

_____

e) How is bad debt shown on the financial statements?

_____

_____

_____

_____

f) How can bad debt be minimized?

_____

_____

_____

_____

_____

_____

_____

_____

_____

g) Which reports are helpful in analyzing a company's accounts receivable?

_____

_____

_____

_____

_____

_____

h) What is an aging list?

_____

_____

_____

_____

_____

_____

i) What is the difference between a credit sale and a cash sale?

_____

_____

_____

_____

_____

_____

j)   How can you assess the quality of accounts receivable?

_____

_____

_____

_____

k)   What is the impact of selling on credit and what is the potential risk involved?

_____

_____

_____

_____

l)   How would one determine if the bad debt estimate for a new company is reasonable? Should desired net income be used as the basis for estimating bad debt?

_____

_____

_____

_____

_____

_____

_____

_____

_____

_____

_____

_____

Notes

Chapter 3

LONG-TERM ASSETS

LEARNING OUTCOMES

❶ Identify the characteristics of long-term assets

❷ Record the acquisition and changes in the value of property, plant and equipment

❸ Apply the three methods of depreciation of property, plant and equipment

❹ Account for the gain or loss on disposal of asset and changes in depreciation estimates

❺ Account for natural resources

❻ Define and account for intangible assets and describe the different types of intangible assets

❼ Calculate and interpret asset turnover and return on asset ratios

❽ Describe controls related to long-term assets

❾ Describe ethical approach related to long-term assets

AMEENGAGE™ *Access **ameengage.com** for integrated resources including tutorials, practice exercises, the digital textbook and more.*

Assessment Questions

AS-1 (❶)

Where are long-term assets listed on the balance sheet?

_____

_____

_____

AS-2 (❶)

Define long-term assets. Give an example of a long-term asset.

_____

_____

_____

_____

AS-3 (❶)

What are the three characteristics of long-term assets?

_____

_____

_____

_____

_____

AS-4 (❷)

What is meant by a lump sum purchase of assets? How are costs allocated when the purchase of assets is a lump sum purchase?

_____

_____

_____

_____

_____

AS-5 (❷)

After the initial purchase of a long-term asset, additional costs may be incurred. What criteria are used to assess whether these costs are regarded as an expense or an addition to assets?

_____

_____

_____

_____

_____

_____

_____

_____

_____

AS-6 (❸)

What is the residual value of a long-term asset?

_____

_____

_____

AS-7 (❸)

Name three different methods of calculating depreciation.

_____

_____

_____

_____

AS-8 (❹)

Does a company always receive the estimated salvage value of an asset on disposal? Assuming the asset is fully depreciated, how is the difference between the estimated residual value and the actual salvage value treated?

_____

_____

_____

_____

AS-9 (❹)

What does the net book value of a long-term asset represent? Does the net book value represent the actual value of the asset?

_____

_____

_____

_____

AS-10 (⊙)

In which section of the balance sheet are intangible assets found?

_____

_____

_____

AS-11 (⊙)

What is the primary difference between intangible assets and tangible assets?

_____

_____

_____

_____

_____

AS-12 (⊙)

Define intangible assets and describe the costs that are included in calculating their value.

_____

_____

_____

_____

AS-13 (⊙)

Define goodwill.

_____

_____

_____

_____

AS-14 (6)

How is the value of goodwill calculated?

_____

_____

_____

AS-15 (6)

What is the major difference between goodwill and other intangible assets?

_____

_____

_____

AS-16 (5)

What method is usually used to record the depletion of natural resources?

_____

_____

_____

AS-17 (4)

How is the per unit amount for units-of-production depreciation calculated?

_____

_____

_____

AS-18 (6)

List three examples of intangible assets.

_____

_____

_____

AS-19 (❽)

How can a company protect the value of its intangible assets?

_____

_____

_____

AS-20 (❾)

True or False: In the year that a company has high taxable income, its accountant should help to minimize the company's tax obligations by classifying long-term asset items as expense items.

_____

_____

_____

_____

AS-21 (❹)

What is impairment?

_____

_____

_____

AS-22 (❹)

What is the recoverable amount when it comes to asset impairment?

_____

_____

_____

AS-23 (❺)

In a natural resource company, what do assets under construction mainly represent?

_____

_____

_____

_____

AS-24 (❺)

True or False: Depletion of assets should start as soon the asset is under construction.

_____

_____

_____

AS-25 (❹)

Where does an impairment loss appear on the income statement?

_____

_____

_____

AS-26 (❼)

What does the asset turnover ratio measure?

_____

_____

AS-27 (❼)

What does the return on assets ratio measure?

_____

_____

Application Questions Group A

AP-1A (❷)

Prepare the journal entry for the purchase of machinery worth $200,000 (on credit) on March 6, 2016.

Date	Account Title and Explanation	Debit	Credit

AP-2A (❸)

Prepare the journal entry to record depreciation of $2,000 for a long-term asset on February 29, 2016.

Date	Account Title and Explanation	Debit	Credit

AP-3A (❷)

Land, building and equipment were purchased for a total amount of $800,000 on May 25, 2016. The assessed values of these purchases were, Land—$600,000; Building—$300,000; Equipment—$100,000. Calculate the cost of each asset by filling in the following table, and write the journal entry that records the purchase.

Item	Assessment	Percent	Applied to Cost

Date	Account Title and Explanation	Debit	Credit

AP-4A (❸ ❹)

On July 1, 2008, Bob's Juice Factory purchased a bottle-sealing machine for $102,000. The machine had an estimated useful life of 10 years and is expected to have no residual value. Assume that the company has adopted a partial-year depreciation policy, where depreciation is taken on a monthly basis.

Required

a) Fill in the table below using the following facts:

- The company uses straight-line depreciation.

- The company's fiscal year-end is December 31.

- The company stopped using this machine on November 1, 2016, when it was traded for a new machine

Year	Cost of Long-Term Asset	Depreciation Expense	Accumulated Depreciation To Date	Net Book Value

b) On November 1, 2016, Bob's Juice Factory traded the old bottle-sealing machine for a new machine. The price tag on the new machine is $130,000. In return for the old machine that Bob's Juice Factory is giving up, the supplier of the new machine agrees to take $30,000 off the price of the new machine even though the fair value of the old machine on the day of the trade is only $20,000. Record the journal entry for the machine exchange.

Date	Account Title and Explanation	Debit	Credit

Analysis

What is a drawback of using the straight-line depreciation method?

_____

_____

_____

_____

_____

_____

AP-5A (❸ ❹)

Equipment was purchased on December 31, 2012 for $50,000. The asset is expected to last for four years, at which time the estimated residual value will be $10,000.

Required

a) Prepare a table showing the year, the cost of the asset, the amount of depreciation expense each year, accumulated depreciation to date and net book value. The company uses straight-line depreciation.

Year	Cost of Long-Term Asset	Depreciation Expense	Accumulated Depreciation To Date	Net Book Value

b) The asset was sold for $12,000 cash on the first day of 2017. Prepare the journal entry to record the sale.

Date	Account Title and Explanation	Debit	Credit

c) Using the same purchase information at the beginning of the question, prepare the table assuming that the company used double-declining-balance depreciation and the asset had no residual value.

Year	Net Book Value at the Beginning of the Year	Depreciation Expense	Accumulated Depreciation To Date	Net Book Value at the End of the Year

d) Using the same purchase information and residual value at the beginning of the question, assume that the company uses the units-of-production method. The asset can produce one million units. Record of production: year 2013—300,000 units; year 2014—250,000; year 2015—300,000 units; year 2016—100,000 units. Prepare a table showing the year, the cost of the asset, the amount of depreciation expense each year, accumulated depreciation to date and net book value. (Hint: Depreciate the cost of the asset minus its residual value.)

Year	Cost of Long-Term Asset	Depreciation Expense	Accumulated Depreciation To Date	Net Book Value

Analysis

Since the double-declining balance method for depreciation allows charging higher depreciation in the first few years, some business owners may want to use this method for all assets. Is it appropriate to use this method for all assets?

_____

_____

_____

_____

_____

_____

_____

_____

_____

AP-6A (❸)

On January 1, 2013 a long-term asset was purchased for $50,000. The asset was expected to last for four years (with an estimated residual value of $10,000). For the first two years, the company used the double-declining-balance. Suppose the company decides to switch to the straight–line method after recording the depreciation expense for 2014. Calculate the depreciation expense for the years 2015 and 2016.

_____

_____

_____

_____

_____

_____

_____

_____

_____

_____

AP-7A (❸ ❹)

On December 31, 2010, Tiesto Company purchased equipment worth $150,000. The equipment has a useful life of six years and no residual value. Depreciation is recorded beginning a month after acquisition and will be recorded up until the month of disposal. The company uses the straight-line method of depreciation.

Required

a) Given that the company's year-end is December 31, complete the following table.

Year	Cost of Long-Term Asset	Depreciation Expense	Accumulated Depreciation To Date	Net Book Value

b) On June 30, 2016, Tiesto Company sold the equipment for $3,000. Prepare a journal entry to record the depreciation on the disposal and the sale. You will need to recalculate the depreciation expense for 2016 from part a) to account for the sale part-way during the year.

Date	Account Title and Explanation	Debit	Credit

Analysis

The owner of Tiesto Company believes that the loss on sale of equipment indicates that the company has made a mistake while calculating depreciation. Do you agree or disagree? Explain.

_____

_____

_____

AP-8A (❸ ❹)

At the beginning of 2015, an entrepreneur purchased a group of assets as a "bulk purchase" at an auction sale. The entrepreneur paid $250,000 "as is" for two automobiles, a widget machine, a forklift truck and a trailer. The items were valued by a professional appraiser as follows.

Item	Estimated Value	Percentage	Estimated Remaining Life
Auto 1	$10,000	3.22%	3 Years
Auto 2	15,000	4.84%	5 Years
Widget Machine	258,000	83.23%	15 Years
Forklift	15,000	4.84%	5 Years
Trailer	12,000	3.87%	10 Years
Total	310,000	100%	

After the auction, the entrepreneur had the machine moved to the factory. Moving the widget machine cost $2,000. After the machine was placed in the factory, an electrician was contracted to install additional power lines and hook up the machine at a cost of $1,000. A plumber was also needed to connect the machine to the water mains. This cost $500. A gas fitter was required to connect the widget machine to the gas line at a cost of $200.

Before placing Auto 1 and 2 into use, the entrepreneur took both autos to the local repair shop. The mechanic said that Auto 1 needed a new engine that would cost $2,000 and Auto 2 needed a major tune-up at a cost of $500 (the tune-up is required to get the car going). The entrepreneur paid cash for the repairs. Early in 2016, the entrepreneur advertised and sold Auto 1 for $8,000 and replaced the front brakes on Auto 2 for $300.

The entrepreneur's company uses a half-year method for depreciation (i.e. ½ year's depreciation in the year of purchase, and ½ year's depreciation in the year of sale). The company uses straight-line depreciation, with an estimated residual value of 10% of cost for all assets.

Required

Write the journal entries to record the following.

a) Using straight-line depreciation method, record all journal entries related to the above transactions. When allocating a bulk purchase, round up to the nearest dollar. If necessary, adjust the largest number up or down to avoid journal entry imbalance due to rounding. Note: The exact journal entry dates can be omitted for the purpose of this exercise. Simply indicate if each transaction belongs to 2015 or 2016.

Date	Account Title and Explanation	Debit	Credit

Date	Account Title and Explanation	Debit	Credit

Date	Account Title and Explanation	Debit	Credit

b) Using the double-declining-balance depreciation method, redo the journal entries for the depreciation of the Trailer for 2015 and 2016. Note: the exact journal entry dates can be omitted for the purpose of this exercise. Simply indicate if each transaction belongs to 2015 or 2016. Show your calculations in the space provided on the following page.

Date	Account Title and Explanation	Debit	Credit

_____

_____

_____

_____

_____

_____

_____

_____

AP-9A (❻)

Feggins Company purchased a patent from Marquette Limited for $200,000 on January 1, 2016. The patent has a remaining life of six years.

Required

a) Prepare the journal entry to record the purchase.

Date	Account Title and Explanation	Debit	Credit

b) Prepare the journal entry to record amortization for one year on December 31, 2016. The company does not use the half-year rule. Assume the straight-line method of depreciation is used.

Date	Account Title and Explanation	Debit	Credit

AP-10A (0)

Mirabella Manufacturing spent several years developing a process for producing widgets. Its lawyer suggested patenting the process. The company obtained the patent on January 1, 2016. The company paid $100,000 to the lawyer, $25,000 to the government for the patent and $10,000 in additional fees.

Required

a) Prepare the journal entries to record the cost of the patent.

Date	Account Title and Explanation	Debit	Credit

b) The patent has a life of 20 years. Prepare the journal entry to amortize the patent for one year on December 31, 2016.

Date	Account Title and Explanation	Debit	Credit

AP-11A (❺)

Turpen Corporation purchased a large forest for $12 million on January 1, 2016. Turpen estimates that 10 million board feet (BF) of lumber can be harvested. After 10 years, Turpen will sell the land and expects it to be worth $2 million.

Required

a) Record the journal entry for the purchase of the forest.

Date	Account Title and Explanation	Debit	Credit

b) Calculate the unit cost for each BF to be extracted.

_____

_____

_____

_____

_____

c) During the current year, the company harvested 500,000 board feet. Record the journal entry to record the harvesting on December 31, 2016.

Date	Account Title and Explanation	Debit	Credit

AP-12A (⑥)

John Partington purchased assets ($500,000) and liabilities ($400,000) of a company, for which he paid $150,000 on August 6, 2016. The company owns the rights to a unique product.

Required

a) Record the purchase transaction.

Date	Account Title and Explanation	Debit	Credit

b) Subsequent to the purchase of the company, a competitor appeared. On December 31, 2016, John assessed that the value of the goodwill that his company owned was now worth $20,000. Record the appropriate journal entry to reflect the reduction in the value of goodwill.

Date	Account Title and Explanation	Debit	Credit

AP-13A (❸)

On July 1, 2015, Earth Corporation purchased factory equipment for $150,000. The equipment is to be depreciated over eight years using the double-declining-balance method. Earth Corporation's year-end is on September 30. Calculate the depreciation expense to be recorded for the year 2016. Earth Corporation depreciates its assets based on the number of months it owned the asset during the year.

AP-14A (❻)

On February 1, 2016, Eastern Company acquired the assets ($800,000) and liabilities ($500,000) of Newton Corporation. The agreed purchase price is $500,000 in cash. Prepare a journal entry to record the purchase.

Date	Account Title and Explanation	Debit	Credit

AP-15A (❻)

On January 1, 2016, Lava Company purchased a $90,000 patent for a new consumer product. However, the patent's useful life is estimated to be only 10 years due to the competitive nature of the product.

Required

a) Prepare a journal entry to record the purchase.

Date	Account Title and Explanation	Debit	Credit

b) Prepare a journal entry to record the amortization on December 31, 2016.

Date	Account Title and Explanation	Debit	Credit

AP-16A (❼)

The following data pertains to Krips Company for the year ended December 31, 2016.

Net Sales	$60,000
Net Income	15,000
Total Assets (January 1, 2016)	200,000
Total Assets (December 31, 2016)	300,000

Calculate Krips Company's return on assets for 2016. Explain what the ratio means.

AP-17A (❸ ❹)

Details of some of Stark Corporation's long-term assets are listed below.

Date of Purchase	Asset	Cost	Residual Value	Estimated Useful Life
Feb 1, 2013	Building	$370,600	$25,000	8 years
Sep 1, 2013	Truck	$51,400	$4,600	6 years

On August 1, 2016, Stark Corporation decides to dispose of both of these assets. The total proceeds received for the assets were $246,000. Both assets use the straight-line depreciation method based on the number of months owned in the year. Stark Corporation has a December 31 year-end. Round all answers to the nearest whole number.

Required

a) Prepare the depreciation table.

Year	Cost of Long-Term Asset	Depreciation Expense	Accumulated Depreciation	Net Book Value
Building				
2013				
2014				
2015				
2016				
Truck				
2013				
2014				
2015				
2016				

b) Prepare the journal entry to record the disposal of the assets.

Date	Account Title and Explanation	Debit	Credit

AP-18A (❷)

On September 8, 2016, Swanson Corporation purchased the following assets: land, machinery and a building. The appraised values of the assets were $1,000,000 for land, $200,000 for machinery and $800,000 for the building. The total purchase price of all three assets was $1,700,000. Swanson paid cash of $365,400 and signed a note payable for the remaining balance.

Required

a) Complete the table to determine the cost of the assets.

Item	Appraised	Percent	Applied to Cost

b) Prepare the journal entry to record the purchase.

Date	Account Title and Explanation	Debit	Credit

AP-19A (❸)

A new machine for a bottle factory was purchased in February 2013 for $900,000. The machine has an estimated production capacity of 1,500,000 bottles and no residual value. The machine produced the following number of bottles over the past four years: 2013 – 420,000 bottles, 2014 – 405,000 bottles, 2015 – 390,000 bottles, 2016 – 315,000 bottles. Assuming the company uses the units-of-production method, complete the following table.

Year	Cost of Long-Term Asset	Depreciation Expense	Accumulated Depreciation To Date	Net Book Value

AP-20A (❸ ❹)

On December 31, 2016, a company had the following information reported in their balance sheet.

Equipment	$400,000
Accumulated Depreciation—Equipment	(320,000)

The equipment was donated to a charity. The equipment was valued at its current net book value. Prepare the journal entry to record the donation.

Date	Account Title and Explanation	Debit	Credit

AP-21A (⑤)

Metallic Inc. is an international producer of aluminum through bauxite mining. It recently spent $5,000,000 cash to purchase a mine with an estimated residual value of zero. The company also incurred additional expenditures of $700,000 in preparing the mine for the extraction of bauxite. Metallic Inc. expects to use this mine for eight years with an expected capacity of 200,000 tons of bauxite over that time.

Required

a) Prepare the journal entry to record the purchase of the bauxite mine.

Date	Account Title and Explanation	Debit	Credit

b) Calculate the unit cost for each ton of bauxite to be extracted.

_____

_____

_____

_____

_____

_____

c) Metallic Inc. extracted 15,000 tons of bauxite in the first year. Prepare the journal entries to record the depletion for this year.

Date	Account Title and Explanation	Debit	Credit

AP-22A (③ ④)

ReHear Company is in the business of producing and selling hearing aid technology. As a result of recent advances in this type of technology, the company decided to test its factory equipment for impairment. Four years ago, the equipment was purchased for $520,000 with an estimated residual value of $40,000. The equipment is expected to have a useful life of 15 years and four years of depreciation have been recorded up to the impairment test. The company uses straight-line depreciation.

Required

a) What is the net book value of the equipment at the end of this year?

b) Was it required for ReHear to implement an impairment test for its equipment? Why?

c) Assume ReHear company finds out that the equipment's recoverable amount is $390,000. Is the equipment impaired? If yes, how much is the impairment loss?

d) Record the journal entry for the impairment loss, if any.

Date	Account Title and Explanation	Debit	Credit

AP-23A (❼)

The following financial data is given for two companies, TIX and SUBA. They are both in the business of selling fresh produce to large supermarkets across North America. Both companies have a year-end of December 31.

TIX Company	December 31, 2015	December 31, 2014
Net Sales	$2,500,000	$2,250,000
Total Assets	$4,700,000	$4,200,000
Net Income	$310,000	$300,000
Gross Profit	$1,000,000	$900,000

SUBA Company	December 31, 2015	December 31, 2014
Net Sales	$1,900,000	$2,200,000
Total Assets	$1,500,000	$1,800,000
Net Income	$400,000	$421,000
Gross Profit	$855,000	$990,000

Required

Based on the information provided, answer the following questions. Round your answers to two decimal places.

a) Calculate the asset turnover of each company for 2015.

_____

_____

_____

_____

_____

_____

b) In 2015, which company performed better when it comes to managing assets? Explain.

_____

_____

_____

_____

_____

Analysis

TIX uses the straight-line method of depreciation and SUBA uses the double-declining-balance method of depreciation. Does this affect your ability to compare these two companies?

_____

_____

_____

_____

_____

_____

_____

_____

_____

_____

AP-24A (⑥)

On February 1, 2016 CN Corporation bought assets and liabilities of Lincoln Inc. for $300,000. CN paid a premium for the purchase because Lincoln Inc. is a recognizable brand in the market. Lincoln had assets of $600,000 and liabilities of $400,000.

Required

a) Prepare the journal entry for CN Corporation to record the purchase of Lincoln Inc.

Date	Account Title and Explanation	Debit	Credit

b) Due to an increase in the number of competitors in the market, on December 31, 2016 CN Corporation reviewed all assets for any impairment. It was discovered that the goodwill has a fair market value of only $85,000. Prepare the journal entry to record this impairment to goodwill.

Date	Account Title and Explanation	Debit	Credit

Application Questions Group B

AP-1B (❷)

On March 1, 2016, Lindt Corp. bought machinery for $250,000 on credit from Super Machines Inc. Prepare the journal entry to record the transaction.

Date	Account Title and Explanation	Debit	Credit

AP-2B (❸)

On June 1, 2013, new equipment was purchased for use in the factory. The equipment cost $1,200,000 and has a salvage value of $180,000. The equipment has an estimated production capacity of 800,000 units. The equipment produced the following number of units over the past four years: 2013—224,000 units, 2014—216,000 units, 2015—208,000 units, and 2016—168,000 units. Assuming the company uses the units-of-production method, complete the following table. Do not round the per unit cost of depreciation in your calculations.

Year	Cost of Long-Term Asset	Depreciation Expense	Accumulated Depreciation To Date	Net Book Value

AP-3B (❷)

On September 5, 2016, land, building and equipment were purchased for a total amount of $1,300,000. The assessed value of each asset at the time of acquisition is as follows: Land—$845,000; Building—$325,000; Equipment—$455,000. Write the journal entry that records the purchase.

Date	Account Title and Explanation	Debit	Credit

AP-4B (❸ ❹)

On April 1, 2008, Bob's Juice Factory purchased a new bottle sealing machine for $99,000. The machine had an estimated useful life of 10 years and is expected to have no residual value. Assume that the company has adopted a partial-year depreciation policy, where depreciation is taken on a monthly basis.

Required

a) Prepare the table using the following facts.
    - The company uses straight line depreciation.
    - The asset is sold on April 30, 2016 for $31,000.
    - The company's fiscal year-end is December 31.

Year	Cost of Long-Term Asset	Depreciation Expense	Accumulated Depreciation To Date	Net Book Value

b) Record the journal entry for the sale, assuming that the depreciation for 2016 has already been recorded.

Date	Account Title and Explanation	Debit	Credit

AP-5B (❸ ❹)

Equipment was purchased on January 1, 2016 for $86,000. The asset is expected to last for four years, at which time the estimated residual value will be $7,000.

Required

a) Fill in the following table, assuming the company uses straight-line depreciation.

Year	Cost of Long-Term Asset	Depreciation Expense	Accumulated Depreciation To Date	Net Book Value

b) Fill in the following table, assuming that the company uses the units-of-production method and that the estimated residual value will be $7,000. The asset is expected to produce a total of 1,010,000 units over four years. The number of units that the asset is expected to produce for each year is: year 2016—202,000 units; year 2017—252,500 units; year 2018—303,000 units; year 2019—252,500 units.

Year	Cost of Long-Term Asset	Depreciation Expense	Accumulated Depreciation To Date	Net Book Value

c) Continuing from part b), the business sold the equipment on December 31, 2019 for $9,000 cash. The sale happened after the journal entry to record the year's depreciation. Prepare the journal entry to record the sale of the equipment.

Date	Account Title and Explanation	Debit	Credit

AP-6B (❸ ❹)

On January 1, 2014, South Company purchased a machine for $40,000. The residual value was estimated to be $5,000. The machine will be depreciated over five years using the straight-line method. The company's year-end is December 31.

Required

a) Prepare a depreciation schedule for the machine's useful life using the following table.

Year	Cost of Long-Term Asset	Depreciation Expense	Accumulated Depreciation To Date	Net Book Value

b) At the end of 2018, the company stopped using this machine. Since no one was interested in buying it, the machine was simply discarded. Prepare a journal entry to record the machine's retirement.

Date	Account Title and Explanation	Debit	Credit

c) Assume that South Company uses the double-declining-balance depreciation method and the machine has no residual value. At the end of 2018, new technology emerged, making the product manufactured by this machine obsolete. After testing for impairment, South Company determines that the fair value of the machine has permanently declined to $50. Prepare a depreciation schedule for the machine's useful life using the following table. Determine whether impairment has incurred, and if so, calculate the amount of impairment loss.

Year	Net Book Value at the beginning of the year	Depreciation Expense	Accumulated Depreciation To Date	Net Book Value at the end of the year

_____

_____

_____

_____

_____

_____

_____

d) Assume that the company uses the units-of-production method, and the machine can produce 350,000 units. Record of production: 2014—20,000 units; 2015—60,000 units; 2016—70,000 units; 2017—100,000 units; 2018—100,000 units. Prepare a depreciation schedule for the machine's useful life using the following table. Compare the pattern of depreciation expense resulting from three different depreciation methods in parts a), c) and d).

Year	Cost of Long-Term Asset	Depreciation Expense	Accumulated Depreciation To Date	Net Book Value

_____

_____

_____

_____

AP-7B (❸ ❹)

MNO Company purchased equipment worth $35,000 on January 1, 2016. The equipment has an estimated five-year service life with no residual value. The company's policy for five-year assets is to use the double-declining-balance method for the first two years of the asset's life and then switch to the straight-line depreciation method. The company's year-end is December 31.

Required

a) Calculate the depreciation expense on December 31, 2018.

_____

_____

_____

_____

_____

b) Assume that MNO Company's depreciation policy recognizes only half a year's depreciation in the year of purchase and half a year's depreciation in the year of disposal. The company uses the straight-line method. The asset was sold for $15,000 on May 15, 2018. Prepare a depreciation schedule using the following table.

Year	Cost of Long-Term Asset	Depreciation Expense	Accumulated Depreciation To Date	Net Book Value

c) Prepare the journal entry to record the depreciation on the disposal and sale.

Date	Account Title and Explanation	Debit	Credit

AP-8B (❸)

Leonard Corporation acquired a machine in the first week of October 2015 and paid the following bills.

Invoice Price	$40,000
Freight In	5,000
Installation Cost	7,000

The estimated useful life of the machine is eight years with no residual value. The company has December 31 as its year-end and uses a straight-line depreciation method to depreciate long-term assets. Leonard Corporation depreciates their assets based on the number of months they owned the asset during the year.

Required

a) Calculate the book value of the machine on December 31, 2016.

b) On December 31 2016, the business sold the machine for $40,000. The sale happened after the journal entry to record the year's depreciation. Prepare the journal entry to record the sale of the machine.

Date	Account Title and Explanation	Debit	Credit

AP-9B (⑥)

On September 1, 2015, Pat Jarvis purchased assets ($492,000) and liabilities ($422,000) of a company, for which he paid $200,000. The extra amount was paid because the company sells a superior product.

Required

a)   Record the purchase transaction.

Date	Account Title and Explanation	Debit	Credit

b)   Subsequent to the purchase of the company, a competitor appeared. On August 31, 2016, Pat assessed the value of the goodwill that his company owned was now worth $113,000. Record the appropriate journal entry to reflect the reduction in the value of goodwill.

Date	Account Title and Explanation	Debit	Credit

AP-10B (6)

Higgins Company purchased a patent from Marquette Limited for $283,000 on August 1, 2015. The patent has a remaining life of six years.

Required

a) Prepare the journal entry to record the purchase.

Date	Account Title and Explanation	Debit	Credit

b) Prepare the journal entry to record amortization for one year on July 31, 2016. The company does not use the half-year rule.

Date	Account Title and Explanation	Debit	Credit

AP-11B (5)

On March 1, 2016, Bowser Mining purchased an ore mine for $3,000,000. The company expects to use the mine for five years and expects to extract 100,000 tons of ore over that time. At the end of five years, the residual value is estimated to be $500,000. For the year ended December 31, 2016, the company extracted 16,000 tons of ore. Prepare the journal entry to record the depletion for 2016.

Date	Account Title and Explanation	Debit	Credit

AP-12B (❻)

On August 1, 2016, Watertown Inc. purchased a trademark from Savanah Corp. for $410,000. The company paid $265,000 cash and issued a note payable for the remaining balance. The trademark has a useful life of 12 years but Watertown plans to sell the trademark after eight years because it anticipates technological changes in the market that will render the trademark obsolete.

Required

a) Prepare the journal entry for the purchase of the trademark and the entry required to record amortization for the first year on December 31, 2016.

Date	Account Title and Explanation	Debit	Credit

b) Prepare the journal entry to record amortization for the second year on December 31, 2017.

Date	Account Title and Explanation	Debit	Credit

AP-13B (❻)

On January 1, 2016, Singleton Corporation purchased the assets and liabilities of Twinning's Inc. for a total purchase price of $215,800. Singleton paid a premium for the purchase, because Twinning's products are a recognizable brand name in the market. Twinning's had assets of $847,000 and liabilities of $674,900.

Required

a) Prepare the journal entry for Singleton to record the purchase.

Date	Account Title and Explanation	Debit	Credit

b) Due to an increase in the number of competitors in the market, on December 31, 2016 Singleton reviewed all assets for any impairment. It was discovered that the goodwill had a fair market value of only $36,500. Record the journal entry to record this impairment to goodwill.

Date	Account Title and Explanation	Debit	Credit

AP-14B (6)

Turnbull Inc. purchased the assets ($516,800) and liabilities ($407,600) of Chapman Inc. on May 1, 2016 for a total purchase price of $315,000. Turnbull paid $105,000 in cash and signed a note payable for the remaining balance. This is an exciting transaction for Turnbull, as it will be acquiring Chapman's employees, a very experienced and skilled workforce.

Required

a) Prepare the journal entry for Turnbull to record the purchase.

Date	Account Title and Explanation	Debit	Credit

b) Over the year, a number of key personnel have left the company, and through a review of its assets on December 31, 2016, Turnbull has noted impairment in goodwill of $23,000. Record the journal entry to record this impairment to goodwill.

Date	Account Title and Explanation	Debit	Credit

AP-15B (❻)

Gamma Inc. has a December year-end. Gamma purchased a copyright from Delta Corporation for $60,000 cash on March 1, 2016. The copyright allows the owners' rights for five years. Gamma uses the straight-line method to amortize intangible assets.

Required

a) Prepare the journal entry for the purchase of the copyright and the entry required to record amortization for the first year on December 31, 2016.

Date	Account Title and Explanation	Debit	Credit

b) Prepare the journal entry to record amortization for the second year on December 31, 2017.

Date	Account Title and Explanation	Debit	Credit

Analysis

Intangible assets do not have any physical form. Why are they considered assets?

_____

_____

_____

AP-16B (❼)

Joe Corporation's selected financial data is given below.

Net Sales for 2016	$180,000
Cost of Sales for 2016	99,000
Average Total Assets for 2016	120,000

Calculate the company's asset turnover. Explain what the ratio means.

_____

_____

_____

_____

_____

_____

_____

_____

_____

_____

_____

_____

AP-17B (❸ ❹)

Details of some of Lannister Inc.'s long-term assets are listed below.

Date of Purchase	Asset	Cost	Residual Value	Estimated Useful Life
Mar 30, 2013	Equipment	$127,800	$18,000	10 years
Jul 1, 2013	Machinery	$95,800	$25,000	12 years

On April 30, 2016, Lannister Inc. decides to dispose of both of these assets. The total proceeds received for the assets were $180,000. Both assets use the straight-line depreciation method based on the number of months owned in the year. Lannister Inc. has a December 31 year-end. Round all answers to the nearest whole number.

Required

a) Prepare the depreciation table.

Year	Cost of Long-Term Asset	Depreciation Expense	Accumulated Depreciation	Net Book Value
Equipment				
2013				
2014				
2015				
2016				
Machinery				
2013				
2014				
2015				
2016				

b) Prepare the journal entry to record the disposal of the assets.

Date	Account Title and Explanation	Debit	Credit

AP-18B (❷)

Patterson Inc. purchased land, land improvements and a building on May 15, 2016 from StarGen Inc. The appraised values of the assets were $740,000 for land, $100,000 for land improvements and $160,000 for the building. Patterson Inc. paid $530,000 in cash and signed a note payable for the remaining balance of $370,000.

Required

a) Complete the table to determine the cost of the assets.

Item	Appraised	Percent	Applied to Cost

b) Prepare the journal entry to record the purchase.

Date	Account Title and Explanation	Debit	Credit

AP-19B (❸)

On January 1, 2013, Cutie Company purchased a piece of equipment for $90,000 and depreciated it by using the straight-line method. The company estimated that the equipment had a useful life of eight years with no residual value. On January 1, 2016, Cutie determined that the equipment only had a useful life of six years from the date of acquisition with no residual value.

Calculate the accumulated depreciation as of December 31, 2016. Explain why the yearly amortization for 2016 is different from the three preceding years.

_____

_____

_____

_____

_____

_____

_____

_____

_____

_____

AP-20B (❸ ❹)

On January 1, 2014, a company purchased equipment for $22,400. It is expected to last for four years and have a residual value of $9,600. The equipment is donated to a local charity on December 31, 2016 and valued at $12,800. Prepare the journal entry required to record the donation. The company uses straight-line depreciation.

Date	Account Title and Explanation	Debit	Credit

AP-21B (⑤)

On January 1, 2015, WeOil Company installed an oil well at a purchase price of $40 million in addition to an installation cost of $5 million, all for cash. The residual value of the oil well is $3 million. WeOil Company estimates that the total predicted output is 75,000 barrels of oil. The company only pumped out 2,000 barrels in 2015 and 3,500 barrels in 2016.

Required

a) Prepare the journal entry to record the purchase of the oil well.

Date	Account Title and Explanation	Debit	Credit

b) Calculate the unit cost for each barrel to be extracted.

_____

_____

c) Prepare the journal entries to record the depletion for 2015.

Date	Account Title and Explanation	Debit	Credit

d) Prepare the journal entries to record the depletion for 2016.

Date	Account Title and Explanation	Debit	Credit

Analysis

If the total estimated barrels of oil extracted changes during the life of the natural resources, is it still suitable to use units-of-production method? Explain why.

_____

_____

_____

_____

_____

_____

_____

AP-22B (❸ ❹)

AIT Company is a well-known producer of activeware including sports shirts and fleeces. On April 2, 2015, AIT Company bought an item of machinery for $120,000 with an expected useful life of 10 years and residual value of zero. AIT Company uses straight-line depreciation and its year-end is December 31. The impairment test was done on December 31, 2018, after taking into account the depreciation expense for the year. After conducting an impairment test on its machinery, AIT realized that the asset has been impaired by $5,000.

Required

a) Record the journal entry for the impairment loss.

Date	Account Title and Explanation	Debit	Credit

b) Calculate the recoverable amount of the machinery on December 31, 2018.

_____

_____

_____

_____

_____

_____

_____

_____

Analysis

How might AIT Company determine the recoverable amount of the machinery at December 31, 2018? Does the company need to test the assets for impairment every year?

_____

_____

_____

_____

_____

AP-23B (❼)

The following financial data is given for two companies, LIN and WOK. They both manufacture and sell office furniture across the US and Canada. Both companies have a year-end of June 30.

LIN Company	June 30, 2015	June 30, 2014
Net Sales	$3,500,000	$3,000,000
Total Assets	$2,200,000	$1,150,000
Net Income	$590,000	$500,000
Gross Profit	$1,575,000	$1,350,000

WOK Company	June 30, 2015	June 30, 2014
Net Sales	$4,500,000	$4,120,000
Total Assets	$5,500,000	$4,800,000
Net Income	$840,000	$620,000
Gross Profit	$1,575,000	$1,442,000

Required

Based on the information provided, answer the following questions. Round your final answers to the nearest whole percentage.

a) Calculate the return on assets for each company in 2015.

_____

_____

_____

_____

_____

_____

_____

_____

_____

_____

b) In 2015, which company performed better when it comes to managing assets? Explain.

_____

_____

_____

_____

c) Assume LIN Company's total assets in 2013 were the same as its total assets in 2014. Did LIN perform better in managing its long-term assets in 2014 or 2015? Why?

_____

_____

_____

_____

_____

_____

_____

_____

_____

_____

_____

AP-24B (❸ ❹)

A company purchased equipment for $50,000 on March 1, 2015. It is expected to last for four years and have a residual value of $10,000. Assume that the company has adopted a partial-year depreciation policy, wherein half a year's depreciation is taken in the year of purchase, and half a year's depreciation is recorded in the year of disposal. The asset is sold on January 18, 2017 for $20,000.

Required

a) Prepare the depreciation table. The company uses straight-line depreciation.

Year	Cost of Long-Term Asset	Depreciation Expense	Accumulated Depreciation To Date	Net Book Value

b) Prepare the journal entry to record the sale.

Date	Account Title and Explanation	Debit	Credit

Case Study

CS-1 (❸)

Canadian National Railway (CNR) and Canadian Pacific Railway (CP) are two companies in the same industry. The relevant portions of their financial statements are provided on the following pages.

Required

a) Using the financial statements provided on the following pages, complete the table for CNR and CP for each item listed in the first column. For the last item, assume that each company added $1 million of rails and calculate the amount of depreciation for one year. (Hint: Assume that the rails are in first position. Use the average estimated years of service life for CP.)

December 31, 2014

Item	CNR	CP
Total Long-Term Assets, Net of Accumulated Depreciation		
Method		
Rate		
Depreciation on $1MM		

b) Why do you think CNR and CP use different rates of depreciation?

_____

_____

_____

_____

_____

_____

_____

_____

_____

_____

_____

Canadian National Railway

The long-term asset portion of Canadian National Railway's Balance Sheet is presented underneath the current assets section, as shown below.

Consolidated Balance Sheet

In millions	December 31,	2014	2013
Assets			
Current assets			
Cash and cash equivalents		$ 52	$ 214
Restricted cash and cash equivalents *(Note 10)*		463	448
Accounts receivable *(Note 6)*		928	815
Material and supplies		335	274
Deferred and receivable income taxes *(Note 4)*		163	137
Other		125	89
Total current assets		2,066	1,977
Properties *(Note 7)*		28,514	26,227
Pension asset *(Note 12)*		882	1,662
Intangible and other assets *(Note 8)*		330	297
Total assets		$ 31,792	$ 30,163

Below is Canadian National Railway's Note 7.

Notes to Consolidated Financial Statements

7 Properties

| | Depreciation | December 31, 2014 | | | December 31, 2013 | | |
In millions	rate	Cost	Accumulated depreciation	Net	Cost	Accumulated depreciation	Net
Properties including capital leases							
Track and roadway [1]	2%	$ 29,995	$ 7,332	$ 22,663	$ 27,833	$ 7,103	$ 20,730
Rolling stock	5%	5,552	2,107	3,445	5,193	1,894	3,299
Buildings	2%	1,545	560	985	1,392	521	871
Information technology [2]	11%	1,068	492	576	1,000	455	545
Other	5%	1,549	704	845	1,388	606	782
Total properties including capital leases		$ 39,709	$ 11,195	$ 28,514	$ 36,806	$ 10,579	$ 26,227
Capital leases included in properties							
Track and roadway [3]		$ 417	$ 63	$ 354	$ 417	$ 58	$ 359
Rolling stock		808	292	516	982	358	624
Buildings		109	23	86	109	21	88
Other		108	29	79	102	22	80
Total capital leases included in properties		$ 1,442	$ 407	$ 1,035	$ 1,610	$ 459	$ 1,151

(1) Includes $2,079 million and $1,911 million of land as at December 31, 2014 and December 31, 2013, respectively.

(2) The Company capitalized $102 million in 2014 and $85 million in 2013 of internally developed software costs pursuant to FASB ASC 350-40, Intangibles – Goodwill and Other, Internal – Use Software.

(3) Includes $108 million of right-of-way access in both years.

Canadian National Railway disclosed its depreciation policy in Note 1 (summary of significant accounting policies), as shown below.

Accounting policy for depreciation

Railroad properties are carried at cost less accumulated depreciation including asset impairment write-downs. The cost of properties, including those under capital leases, net of asset impairment write-downs, is depreciated on a straight-line basis over their estimated service lives, measured in years, except for rail which is measured in millions of gross ton miles. The Company follows the group method of depreciation whereby a single composite depreciation rate is applied to the gross investment in a class of similar assets, despite small differences in the service life or salvage value of individual property units within the same asset class. The Company uses approximately 40 different depreciable asset classes.

For all depreciable assets, the depreciation rate is based on the estimated service lives of the assets. Assessing the reasonableness of the estimated service lives of properties requires judgment and is based on currently available information, including periodic depreciation studies conducted by the Company. The Company's U.S. properties are subject to comprehensive depreciation studies as required by the Surface Transportation Board (STB) and are conducted by external experts. Depreciation studies for Canadian properties are not required by regulation and are conducted internally. Studies are performed on specific asset groups on a periodic basis. Changes in the estimated service lives of the assets and their related composite depreciation rates are implemented prospectively.

The service life of the rail asset is based on expected future usage of the rail in its existing condition, determined using railroad industry research and testing (based on rail characteristics such as weight, curvature and metallurgy), less the rail asset's usage to date. The annual composite depreciation rate for rail assets is determined by dividing the estimated annual number of gross tons carried over the rail by the estimated service life of the rail measured in millions of gross ton miles. The Company amortizes the cost of rail grinding over the remaining life of the rail asset, which includes the incremental life extension generated by rail grinding.

Canadian Pacific Railway

The long-term asset portion of Canadian Pacific Railway's Balance Sheet is presented underneath the current asset portion, as shown below.

CONSOLIDATED BALANCE SHEETS

As at December 31 (in millions of Canadian dollars except common shares)	2014	2013
Assets		
Current assets		
Cash and cash equivalents (Note 11)	$ 226	$ 476
Restricted cash and cash equivalents (Note 19)	–	411
Accounts receivable, net (Note 12)	702	580
Materials and supplies	177	165
Deferred income taxes (Note 7)	56	344
Other current assets	116	53
	1,277	2,029
Investments (Note 14)	112	92
Properties (Note 15)	14,438	13,327
Assets held for sale (Notes 3 and 13)	182	222
Goodwill and intangible assets (Note 16)	176	162
Pension asset (Note 24)	304	1,028
Other assets (Notes 17 and 32)	151	200
Total assets	$ 16,640	$ 17,060

Below is Canadian Pacific Railway's Note 15.

15 Properties

(in millions of Canadian dollars)	2014 Average annual depreciation rate	2014 Cost	2014 Accumulated depreciation	2014 Net book value	2013 Cost	2013 Accumulated depreciation	2013 Net book value
Track and roadway	2.5%	$ 14,515	$ 4,126	$ 10,389	$ 13,459	$ 3,877	$ 9,582
Buildings	3.1%	571	150	421	535	138	397
Rolling stock	2.3%	3,737	1,414	2,323	3,466	1,338	2,128
Information systems[1]	12.4%	631	297	334	679	338	341
Other	4.5%	1,489	518	971	1,372	493	879
Total		$ 20,943	$ 6,505	$ 14,438	$ 19,511	$ 6,184	$ 13,327

[1] During 2014, CP capitalized costs attributable to the design and development of internal-use software in the amount of $69 million (2013 – $85 million; 2012 – $105 million). Current year depreciation expense related to internal use software was $70 million (2013 – $84 million; 2012 – $78 million).

Canadian Pacific Railway disclosed its depreciation policy in Note 1 (summary of significant accounting policies), as shown below.

Properties

Fixed asset additions and major renewals are recorded at cost, including direct costs, attributable indirect costs and carrying costs, less accumulated depreciation and any impairment. When there is a legal obligation associated with the retirement of property, a liability is initially recognized at its fair value and a corresponding asset retirement cost is added to the gross book value of the related asset and amortized to expense over the estimated term to retirement. The Company reviews the carrying amounts of its properties whenever changes in circumstances indicate that such carrying amounts may not be recoverable based on future undiscounted cash flows. When such properties are determined to be impaired, recorded asset values are revised to their fair value.

The Company recognizes expenditures as additions to properties or operating expenses based on whether the expenditures increase the output or service capacity, lower the associated operating costs or extend the useful life of the properties and whether the expenditures exceed minimum physical and financial thresholds.

Much of the additions to properties, both new and replacement properties, are self-constructed. These are initially recorded at cost, including direct costs and attributable indirect costs, overheads and carrying costs. Direct costs include, among other things, labour costs, purchased services, equipment costs and material costs. Attributable indirect costs and overheads include incremental long-term variable costs resulting from the execution of capital projects. Indirect costs include largely local crew facilities, highway vehicles, work trains and area management costs. Overheads primarily include a portion of the cost of the Company's engineering department which plans, designs and administers these capital projects. These costs are allocated to projects by applying a measure consistent with the nature of the cost based on cost studies. For replacement properties, the project costs are allocated to dismantling and installation based on cost studies. Dismantling work is performed concurrently with the installation.

Ballast programs including undercutting, shoulder ballasting and renewal programs which form part of the annual track program are capitalized as this work, and the related added ballast material, significantly improves drainage which in turn extends the life of ties and other track materials. These costs are tracked separately from the underlying assets and depreciated over the period to the next estimated similar ballast program. Spot replacement of ballast is considered a repair which is expensed as incurred.

The costs of large refurbishments are capitalized and locomotive overhauls are expensed as incurred, except where overhauls represent a betterment of the locomotive in which case costs are capitalized.

The Company capitalizes development costs for major new computer systems.

The Company follows group depreciation which groups assets which are similar in nature and have similar economic lives. The property groups are depreciated on a straight-line basis reflecting their expected economic lives determined by studies of historical retirements of properties in the group and engineering estimates of changes in current operations and of technological advances. Actual use and retirement of assets may vary from current estimates, which would impact the amount of depreciation expense recognized in future periods. Rail and other track material in the U.S. are depreciated based directly on usage.

When depreciable property is retired or otherwise disposed of in the normal course of business, the book value, less net salvage proceeds, is charged to accumulated depreciation and if different than the assumptions under the depreciation study could potentially result in adjusted depreciation expense over a period of years. However, when removal costs exceed the salvage value on assets and the Company has no legal obligation to remove the assets, the removal costs incurred are charged to income in the period in which the assets are removed and are not charged to accumulated depreciation.

For the sale or retirement of larger groups of depreciable assets that are unusual and were not considered in depreciation studies, CP records a gain or loss for the difference between net proceeds and net book value of the assets sold or retired.

Equipment under capital lease is included in Properties and depreciated over the period of expected use.

CS-2 (❸ ❻)

Locate the current financial statements of a company that owns intangible assets[1], and supply the following information. Information has been supplied for Pfizer, as an example. (http://www.pfizer.com/system/files/presentation/2014_Pfizer_Financial_Report.pdf)

Note: Most large-cap companies engaged in manufacturing industrial or consumer products will have intangible assets of some sort. You can speed up your search by using a stock filter such as that found at www.globeinvestor.com.

Set the filter as follows.

Industry = industrial products or consumer products
Security = common
Market Capitalization = $5,000 million (minimum)

Example

Item	Answer
Name of company	Pfizer Inc.
Date of financial statements	December 31, 2014
Amount of intangible assets shown on balance sheet	Goodwill—$42,069 million Identifiable Intangible Assets less accumulated amortization—$35,166 million
Total assets	$169,274 million
Intangible assets expressed as a percent of total assets	(42,069 + 35,166) ÷ 169,274 = 46%
Where is there further information about intangibles found on the financial statements?	Note 10
What types of intangible assets does the company own?	Goodwill Developed technology rights Brands License agreements In-process R&D Other
Amount of amortization expense for intangibles for the year	$4,039 million (from income statement)
Amortization expense as percent of profit (continuing operations) before taxes	amortization ÷ (profit + amortization) = 4,039 ÷ (4,039 + 9,119) = 31%
Over what period are intangibles written off? State the source.	Significant accounting policies—note K Identifiable Intangible Assets are written off over their estimated useful life.
Was there any impairment of goodwill or intangibles? State the source.	Yes—as per cash flow statement and note 10.

1 For Canadian company financial statements go to www.sedar.com; for U.S. companies go to http://www.sec.gov/edgar.shtml

Critical Thinking

CT-1 (❷ ❸ ❻)

Grain Eagle Company manufactures and sells pet food. The company has adopted a partial-year depreciation policy, where depreciation is taken on a monthly basis. The company's accounting intern treated the following events that occurred in 2016 as follows.

1) On March 31, 2016, Grain Eagle spent $16 million to purchase land that already comes with a building, which the company will use as a warehouse. The land has a fair value of $12 million and the building has a fair value of $8 million on the date of the purchase. The building has a residual value of $2 million and is expected to bring future economic benefits to the company evenly over its expected useful life of 20 years. Because land and building are acquired together as a bulk purchase and because the building is attached to the land, the intern recorded the $16 million purchase simply as a debit to building and credit to cash.

2) On July 1, 2016, the company purchased a patent at a cost of $500,000. The patent has a legal life of 20 years even though its useful life is expected to be only 10 years. The intern recorded the purchase as a debit to patent and credit to cash of $500,000.

3) On November 30, 2016, the company spent $30,000 on different ingredients as part of research and development. These ingredients will be tested to potentially develop a new pet food formula. The intern capitalized this cost by debiting inventory and crediting cash at $30,000.

4) On December 31, 2016, the company spent $100,000 in legal fees to successfully defend a patent lawsuit. The intern capitalized the $100,000 by debiting patent and crediting cash.

5) On December 31, 2016, the intern recorded depreciation and amortization for all long-term assets, including the building and the patent listed above, and a machine that Grain Eagle acquired on December 31, 2015. The machine costs $200,000, has no residual value, and is expected to produce 2 million kilograms of pet food over its 10 years of useful life. The future economic benefit of the machine depends on the number of kilograms of food it produces, which is expected to vary substantially from year to year. The machine produced 250,000 kilograms of pet food in 2016. Since the intern was not sure which depreciation method she should use, she decided to use the straight-line method for all assets because that is easiest. She recorded depreciation expenses of $20,000 for the machine and $600,000 for the building in 2016. She amortized the patent over the patent's legal life of 20 years. The patent's amortization expense from her calculation is $12,500. The intern recorded depreciation and amortization expenses separately for each asset by debiting depreciation/amortization expenses and crediting accumulated depreciation/amortization.

Required

a) For each of the above events, comment whether the intern's treatment of the event correctly follows accounting standards. If the intern was wrong, suggest what she should have done.

_____

_____

_____

_____

_____

_____

_____

_____

_____

_____

_____

_____

_____

_____

_____

_____

_____

_____

_____

_____

_____

b) Prepare a partial balance sheet as at December 31, 2016 to present the long-term assets and their accumulated depreciation and amortization listed in the events above. Use the correct numbers (not the intern's numbers) in preparing the balance sheet. Assume that the company has no other long-term asset.

c) If Grain Eagle's most important competitor uses the double-declining-balance method in depreciating its long-term assets, should Grain Eagle also use the double-declining-balance method for comparability purpose? Also discuss whether accounting standards should allow only one method rather than allowing multiple methods of depreciation for improved comparability.

_____

_____

_____

_____

_____

_____

_____

_____

_____

_____

_____

_____

_____

_____

_____

_____

_____

_____

_____

_____

_____

_____

CT-2 (6)

Since intangible assets have no physical existence, they cannot be seen. Shareholders may question showing an amount on the balance sheet for an "invisible" asset. Companies have staff with many years of experience who would be difficult to replace, and are therefore deemed valuable. However, the value of such staff is not reflected in the financial statements. Discuss.

Notes

Chapter 4

CURRENT LIABILITIES

LEARNING OUTCOMES

❶ Define and differentiate between determinable and non-determinable liabilities

❷ Record accounts payable

❸ Record payroll liabilities

❹ Record transactions with sales tax

❺ Record unearned revenue

❻ Record short-term notes payable

❼ Record transactions related to the current portion of non-current liabilities

❽ Record estimated liabilities

❾ Apply controls relating to current liabilities

AMEENGAGE *Access **ameengage.com** for integrated resources including tutorials, practice exercises, the digital textbook and more.*

─────── **Assessment Questions** ───────

AS-1 (❶)

What are current liabilities?

_____

_____

_____

AS-2 (❶)

How are non-current liabilities different from current liabilities?

_____

_____

_____

_____

AS-3 (❶)

Explain the main difference between the way assets and liabilities are listed on the balance sheet.

_____

_____

_____

_____

_____

AS-4 (❶)

Should loans payable be presented on the balance sheet as current liabilities or non-current liabilities?

_____

_____

_____

_____

_____

_____

_____

AS-5 (❶)

Define determinable (known) liabilities.

_____

_____

_____

_____

_____

AS-6 (❶)

List at least three examples of determinable (known) liabilities.

_____

_____

_____

_____

_____

AS-7 (❶)

Define non-determinable (unknown) liabilities.

_____

_____

_____

AS-8 (❶)

List at least two examples of non-determinable (unknown) liabilities.

_____

_____

_____

_____

AS-9 (❶)

What is a bank overdraft?

_____

_____

_____

AS-10 (❶)

What is an operating line of credit?

_____

_____

_____

AS-11 (❷)

Which business transaction must have occurred for a company to debit inventory and credit accounts payable in its books?

_____

_____

_____

AS-12 (❷)

True or False: An accounts payable subledger report contains specific information about each customer and the amount owing from each customer.

_____

_____

_____

_____

AS-13 (❷)

List at least three important functions of an accounts payable subledger.

_____

_____

_____

_____

_____

AS-14 (❶)

Why are accrued liabilities considered known liabilities?

_____

_____

_____

_____

AS-15 (❸)

Give an example of accrued liabilities that is common to most businesses.

_____

_____

AS-16 (❸)

How are gross pay and net pay different? Should a company record salaries expense using gross pay or net pay?

_____

_____

_____

AS-17 (❹)

Define sales tax.

_____

_____

_____

_____

AS-18 (❹)

List the three types of sales tax.

_____

_____

_____

_____

_____

AS-19 (❹)

What is the current goods and services tax (GST) rate? Explain how the GST is accounted for by a retailer.

_____

_____

_____

_____

_____

_____

_____

AS-20 (❹)

Why is sales tax not recorded as part of revenue or expenses on a retailer's income statement?

_____

_____

_____

_____

_____

AS-21 (❺)

What is unearned revenue? Why is it a liability? Give two examples of an unearned revenue.

_____

_____

_____

_____

_____

_____

_____

_____

_____

AS-22 (❻)

Explain what a short-term note payable is. List the items you would expect to find on a note payable.

_____

_____

_____

_____

_____

_____

_____

_____

_____

AS-23 (❻)

Describe the journal entries that would be made by the borrower during the period of a short-term note payable.

_____

_____

_____

_____

_____

_____

_____

_____

_____

_____

AS-24 (❻ ❼)

Northing Company has an outstanding 10-year, 5%, $1,000,000 note payable, which was issued on October 31, 2016. Northing must pay $100,000 to the lender on October 31 of each year, starting in 2017. In addition, it must pay interest to the lender semi-annually on April 30 and October 31 of each year. Describe how the note payable and accrued interest should be presented on Northing's financial statements for the year ended December 31, 2016.

_____

_____

_____

_____

_____

_____

_____

_____

_____

AS-25 (❽)

Define "estimated liabilities" and give two examples of them.

_____

_____

_____

_____

AS-26 (❽)

Because it is impossible to predict with 100% certainty the amount of money that a company will have to spend repairing warrantied products, should warranty expense be recorded only when the products are returned for repair? Explain.

_____

_____

_____

_____

_____

AS-27 (❽)

Define "contingent liabilities" and give an example of one.

_____

_____

_____

_____

_____

_____

AS-28 (❽)

Describe how a company accounts for contingent liabilities in its accounting records.

_____

_____

_____

_____

_____

_____

AS-29 (❾)

List some basic practices that a company can implement to control its current liabilities.

_____

_____

_____

_____

_____

_____

_____

AS-30 (❾)

List some possible sources of accounting fraud related to current liabilities, and what a company can do to avoid becoming a victim of fraud.

_____

_____

_____

_____

_____

_____

_____

_____

_____

_____

_____

AS-31 (❽)

Why have customer loyalty programs gained popularity in recent years?

_____

_____

_____

AS-32 (❹)

Explain the use of clearing accounts in the context of sales tax.

_____

_____

_____

_____

_____

AS-33 (❹)

What is the purpose of goods and services tax (GST) recoverable account?

_____

_____

_____

_____

_____

——————— **Application Questions Group A** ———————

AP-1A (❷)

A company has repairs completed on the heating system. The service man hands the accountant an invoice for $1,000 dated May 25, 2017 due in one month. Write the journal entry the company must prepare to record this transaction.

Date	Account Title and Explanation	Debit	Credit

AP-2A (❽)

A company uses substantial amounts of utilities (electricity and water) with an average cost of $6,000 per monthly billing period. They receive and pay the actual bill on the 15th of each month. In January 2017, the company received its bill in the amount of $6,207 for the period December 15 to January 15. The bill was paid right away. Assume the company prepares monthly financial statements.

Required

a) Record the journal entry on December 31, 2016 for the estimate of utilities expense for the period December 16–31, 2016.

b) Record the journal entry required for payment of the bill on January 15, 2017.

Date	Account Title and Explanation	Debit	Credit

AP-3A (❸)

An employer has calculated the following amounts for an employee during the last week of January 2016.

Gross Pay	$1,500
Income Taxes	331
Canada Pension Plan	71
Employment Insurance	28

Required

a) Calculate the employee's net pay.

_____

_____

_____

b) Assuming the employer's contribution is 100% for Canada Pension Plan and 140% for Employment Insurance, what is the employer's portion of CPP and EI?

_____

_____

c) Prepare the journal entries to record payroll for the employee and record the employer's contribution. Assume the employee will not be paid until February 1, 2016.

Date	Account Title and Explanation	Debit	Credit

d) Prepare the journal entry on February 1, 2016 to pay the employee's net pay.

Date	Account Title and Explanation	Debit	Credit

e) Prepare the journal entry on February 15, 2016 to remit all the payroll deductions to the CRA.

Date	Account Title and Explanation	Debit	Credit

AP-4A (❼)

On January 1, 2017, Cervera Company borrowed $100,000 from the local bank. The loan is payable in equal installments over five years. Write the journal entry to record the loan. How much of the loan would be considered current on January 1, 2017?

Date	Account Title and Explanation	Debit	Credit

_____

_____

AP-5A (❼)

On December 31, 2016, Zaharah Company negotiates a loan from the bank for $60,000 with a term of six years, bearing an annual interest rate of 6%. Of this loan, $10,000 plus interest is payable every December 31. Zaharah has a December 31 year-end, and it prepares adjusting entries and financial statements only once a year.

Required

a) Prepare the journal entry to record the cash receipt from loan borrowing.

Date	Account Title and Explanation	Debit	Credit

b) Prepare the journal entry to record the payment of the first installment plus interest on December 31, 2017.

Date	Account Title and Explanation	Debit	Credit

c) What would be the total loan balance on December 31, 2017? How much of the loan would be considered current?

_____

_____

_____

AP-6A (⑥)

NOTE PAYABLE

For the Value Received, the undersigned promises to pay to the order of

_____U. Paymee_____ the sum of

_____ ***** $5,000 and 00/100 Dollars *********************** ($5,000.00) _____

with annual interest of 5% on any unpaid balance. This note shall mature and be payable,

along with accrued interest on:

_____July 31, 2017_____

_____February 1, 2017_____   _____A. Notemaker_____

Issue Date   Borrower Signature

Required

Answer the following questions regarding the note shown above.

a) Who is the lender?

b) Who is the borrower?

c) When is payment due?

d) When was the note issued?

e) When is interest payable?

f) What amount must the borrower pay to the lender?

_____

_____

_____

_____

_____

_____

AP-7A (⊚)

On May 1, 2017, ACME Bank agreed to lend Mirza Enterprises $100,000. Mirza signed a $100,000, 10-month, 12% note. Mirza Enterprises has a year-end of December 31.

Required

Prepare the journal entry for Mirza Enterprises for the following.

a) On the date the note was signed

b) At year-end

c) On March 1, 2018, when the note is repaid

Date	Account Title and Explanation	Debit	Credit

AP-8A (⑥)

On June 15, 2017, Actor Surplus agreed to lend Wei Hong Enterprises $250,000. Wei signed a $250,000, eight-month, 10% note. Wei Hong Enterprises has a year-end of November 30.

Required

Prepare the journal entry for Wei Hong Enterprises for the following.

a) On the date the note was signed

b) At year-end

c) On February 16, 2018, when the note is repaid

Date	Account Title and Explanation	Debit	Credit

AP-9A (❻)

Darren Spoon from Carding Company signed a 7% half-year note payable for $100,000 on November 1, 2017. The note is due with interest on May 1, 2018. Carding Company has a year-end of December 31. Prepare the journal entry for Carding Company for the following.

Required

a) Record the receipt of cash

b) Record accruing interest at the year-end

c) Record ultimate payment of the note in the new year

Date	Account Title and Explanation	Debit	Credit

AP-10A (❺)

The local transit company, in co-operation with local colleges and universities sells transit passes for the semester for $200 each. The passes are only sold prior to the start of the semester, and for the fall semester are good from September 1 to December 31. The transit company sold 1,000 passes on August 1, 2017.

Required

Record the journal entry for the following.

a) The sale of the passes

b) The entry to be recorded on September 30

Date	Account Title and Explanation	Debit	Credit

AP-11A (⑧)

Lee-Yau Enterprises sells heavy-duty lawnmower equipment. On May 4, 2017 it sold a lawnmower (on account) for $45,000 which included a four-year unlimited warranty. The corporation's accountant estimates that $3,000 will be paid out in warranty obligations. The cost of goods sold is $17,000. Assume Lee-Yau uses a perpetual inventory system. Prepare the journal entries relating to these transactions.

Date	Account Title and Explanation	Debit	Credit

AP-12A (❽)

After recording an estimated warranty liability on the sale of a lawnmower, Lee-Yau is required to repair the lawnmower sold (there is a faulty wire) and Lee-Yau spends $500 in cash on October 15, 2017 remedying the problem. Record the journal entry for this transaction.

Date	Account Title and Explanation	Debit	Credit

AP-13A (❽)

Shining Star Corporation produces and sells washing machines, and provides customers with a one-year warranty on all its products. It is estimated that the company incurs approximately $50 of warranty expense on each machine sold. During 2016, the company sold 400 washing machines. All warranty transactions are recorded on December 31.

Required

a) Prepare a journal entry to record the estimated warranty liability.

Date	Account Title and Explanation	Debit	Credit

b) During 2017, the company used $5,000 worth of inventory parts and paid $10,000 for maintenance staff salaries. Prepare a journal entry to record this transaction.

Date	Account Title and Explanation	Debit	Credit

c) At the end of 2017, the company decided to decrease its estimated liability by the remaining balance. Prepare a journal entry to record this transaction.

Date	Account Title and Explanation	Debit	Credit

AP-14A (❽)

Shining Star Corporation provides its customers with an option to purchase a three-year warranty on washing machines. On March 1, 2017, Shining Star received $30,000 cash from customers who purchased the extended warranty for their washing machines.

Required

a) Prepare a journal entry to record the sale of extended warranty on March 1, 2017.

Date	Account Title and Explanation	Debit	Credit

b) Prepare the journal entry required on March 1, 2018.

Date	Account Title and Explanation	Debit	Credit

AP-15A (❼ ❽)

Inline Company sells Spartan laptops for $3,500 each. Each laptop comes with a three-year warranty that requires the corporation to replace defective parts and provide labour. Assume the warranty is honoured equally over the three years. During 2016 the corporation sold 300 laptops. Based on past experience, the estimated average cost for repairs under warranties will be $150 for parts and $200 for labour per laptop sold. During 2017, actual repair cost was $12,000 for parts and $24,000 for labour.

Required

a) Prepare a journal entry on December 31, 2016 to record the estimated warranty liability in 2016.

Date	Account Title and Explanation	Debit	Credit

b) Explain how the warranty liability and expense will appear on the balance sheet and income statement on December 31, 2016.

c) Prepare the journal entry on December 31, 2017 to record the warranty costs for 2017.

Date	Account Title and Explanation	Debit	Credit

d) Explain how the warranty liability and expense will appear on the balance sheet and income statement on December 31, 2017.

_____

_____

_____

_____

_____

_____

_____

Analysis

Discuss why product warranties are recorded as expenses (estimated) at the same time that products are sold, while extended warranties sold to customers are recognized as revenue over several periods.

_____

_____

_____

_____

_____

_____

_____

_____

_____

_____

_____

_____

_____

_____

AP-16A (⑥)

On September 1, 2017, Express Company purchased a delivery truck from MJ Trucks, costing $80,000. However, due to cash flow problems, Express Company is currently unable to make the payment. Therefore, to assure MJ Trucks that it will be paid, Express Company signed a one-year note with 3% interest per annum, to be payable at maturity on August 31, 2018. Express Company's year-end is on December 31. Prepare all the necessary journal entries related to the notes payable from the time it is signed to the maturity date.

Date	Account Title and Explanation	Debit	Credit

Analysis

Businesses are supposed to accrue expenses (such as interest expense) at the end of their fiscal years to report them on their financial statements. Why do you think businesses should not wait until cash is paid to record the expenses?

_____

_____

_____

_____

AP-17A (⑥)

On February 1, 2016, Red Ball received a bank loan for $30,000. The loan bears an interest rate of 2.5% per annum, and will mature in two years. Red Ball has a December 31 year-end. The partial principal of $15,000 plus interest is payable every January 31. Prepare the necessary journal entries from February 1, 2016 to January 31, 2018.

Date	Account Title and Explanation	Debit	Credit

AP-18A (❷ ❺ ❽)

GoodJob Company buys and sells home appliances and uses the perpetual inventory system. GoodJob has a year-end of December 31. During 2017, the company had the following transactions.

Jan 15   Purchased vacuum cleaners worth $60,000 from V Wholesalers, on account.

Feb 4   Sold vacuum cleaners for $45,000 cash, which includes a three-year warranty. GoodJob bought these vacuum cleaners for $30,000.

Feb 4   Recorded $15,000 of estimated warranty liability for the year.

Feb 15   Paid the full amount owing to V Wholesalers.

May 8   Received utilities bill for $3,000, to be paid exactly after 15 days.

May 23   Paid the utilities bill which was received on May 8.

Jul 11   Received $42,000 cash for the sale of vacuum cleaners which cost the company $30,000. The delivery is to be made on August 31.

Aug 31   Delivered the vacuum cleaners from the July 11 transaction.

Prepare journal entries to record the above transactions.

Date	Account Title and Explanation	Debit	Credit

Date	Account Title and Explanation	Debit	Credit

AP-19A (❷ ❹)

Porch Living sells outdoor furniture and accessories. It operates in a province which has a 7% PST and 5% GST. Porch Living charges PST and GST to customers, and pays PST and GST on most purchases, except for inventory. Porch Living only pays GST on the purchase of inventory. The following transactions occurred during May 2017.

May 2   Purchased inventory for $5,000 plus GST on account.

May 5   Sold inventory to a customer for $2,000 plus GST and PST on account. The inventory costs $1,200.

May 12   Purchased $300 worth of office supplies, plus GST and PST in cash.

May 25   Sold inventory to a customer for $6,000 plus GST and PST for cash. The inventory costs $3,200.

May 27   Received the total amount owing from the customer from May 5.

May 28   Paid the supplier from May 2 the amount owing.

May 31   Prepared the PST remittance to the provincial government.

May 31   Prepared the GST remittance to the federal government.

Record the transactions for May 2017.

Date	Account Title and Explanation	Debit	Credit

Date	Account Title and Explanation	Debit	Credit

AP-20A (❷ ❹)

Signet Sales operates in a province where HST is applied to all sales at 13%. During July 2017, it had the following sales.

Jul 10   Sold inventory to a customer for $1,000 plus HST on account.
          The inventory costs $700.

Jul 12   Sold inventory to a customer for $4,000 plus HST for cash.
          The inventory costs $2,900.

Record the transactions for July 2017.

Date	Account Title and Explanation	Debit	Credit

AP-21A (❽)

Canada File is a retail company that sells stationary across Canada. The company offers a customer loyalty program whereby customers are rewarded one cent of "Canada File Money" (CFM) for every $1 purchase. The CFM resembles a real bank note, has no expiry date and can be used by customers as a discount toward future purchases at any Canada File store. In January 2016, Canada File made sales of $400,000. Historically, an average of 75% of CFM issued is redeemed.

Required

a) Prepare the journal entry to record the issuance of CFM in January 2016.

Date	Account Title and Explanation	Debit	Credit

b) In February, Canada File had sales of $500,000, of which $498,000 was received in cash and $2,000 was redeemed using the CFM. Prepare the journal entry to record the sales through cash and CFM redemption in February.

Date	Account Title and Explanation	Debit	Credit

Analysis

In this question, Canada File uses a 75% redemption rate to calculate the amounts for sales discount and redemption rewards liability. What happens if 100% of the rewards were redeemed this year?

_____

_____

_____

_____

_____

_____

_____

_____

AP-22A (❼)

Ricotta Company has the following selected items and balance on their trial balance at December 31, 2017.

Accounts Payable	$9,700
Accounts Receivable	4,200
Cash	5,000
Equipment	65,000
Estimated Warranty Liability	2,500
Inventory	18,400
Prepaid Rent	8,500
Salaries Payable	6,300
Short-term Notes Payable	21,000
Unearned Revenue	8,400

Required

a) Prepare the current liabilities portion of the balance sheet.

b) Based on the information available, calculate the current ratio and comment on the
    liquidity of the company.

_____

_____

_____

_____

_____

Analysis

It is recommended to make use of any purchase discounts that are available. Suppose a
company is offered a discount of 2% for a total payable of $100,000 if payment is made within
30 days. The company does not have enough cash to pay for it within the discount period.
What would you suggest the company do?

_____

_____

_____

_____

_____

Application Questions Group B

AP-1B (❷)

Corrose Company bought equipment worth $10,000 on credit from a supplier. On June 20, the supplier delivered the equipment and sent an invoice, which is due on July 20. Write the journal entry the company must prepare to record the purchase of equipment on June 20.

Date	Account Title and Explanation	Debit	Credit

AP-2B (❸)

Claudia Kusol works for a Canadian marketing firm as a customer service representative. She has the following information for her pay for the week ending September 23, 2016. Her employer contributes 100% toward Canada Pension Plan and 140% toward Employment Insurance.

Hours	38
Hourly Rate	$16.50
Income Tax	$100.32
Canada Pension Plan	$27.70
Employment Insurance	$11.79

Required

a) Prepare the journal entry to record the payroll entry for Claudia Kusol. She will be paid immediately.

Date	Account Title and Explanation	Debit	Credit

b) Prepare the journal entry to record the employer's payroll expense.

Date	Account Title and Explanation	Debit	Credit

c) Prepare the journal entry on October 10, 2016 to record the cash payment for the amount owed to the CRA.

Date	Account Title and Explanation	Debit	Credit

AP-3B (❸)

Jeab Ja Company has calculated the following amounts for the company's office manager, Ricky Marten, during the last week of January 2016.

Gross Pay	$1,800
Income Taxes	445
Canada Pension Plan	86
Employment Insurance	34

Required

a) Calculate Ricky Marten's net pay.

b) Assuming the employer's contribution is 100% for Canada Pension Plan and 140% for Employment Insurance, what is the employer's portion of CPP and EI?

c) Prepare the journal entries to record payroll for Ricky Marten and record Jeab Ja's employer expenses. Assume the employee will not be paid until February 1.

Date	Account Title and Explanation	Debit	Credit

d) Prepare the journal entry on February 1, 2016 to pay the employee his net pay.

Date	Account Title and Explanation	Debit	Credit

e) Prepare the journal entry on February 15, 2016 to remit all the payroll deductions to the CRA.

Date	Account Title and Explanation	Debit	Credit

AP-4B (❼)

On May 1, 2016, Verico Company borrowed $98,000 from the local bank. The loan is payable in equal installments over five years.

Required

a) Write the journal entry to record the loan.

Date	Account Title and Explanation	Debit	Credit

b) How much of the loan would be considered non-current on May 1, 2016?

_____

_____

AP-5B (❼)

On July 1, 2016, Merrit Company borrowed a $200,000 bank loan with a term of four years, bearing an annual interest rate of 5%. Of this loan, $50,000 plus interest is payable every June 30. Merrit has a June 30 year-end, and it prepares adjusting entries and financial statements only once a year.

Required

a) Prepare the journal entry to record the cash receipt from the arranged loan.

Date	Account Title and Explanation	Debit	Credit

b) Prepare the journal entry to record the payment of the first installment plus interest on June 30, 2017.

Date	Account Title and Explanation	Debit	Credit

c) What would be the total loan balance on June 30, 2017? How much of the loan would be considered current?

_____

_____

_____

AP-6B (❻)

On July 1, 2016, Express Company purchased a delivery truck from DW Trucks, costing $85,000. However, due to cash flow problems, Express Company is currently unable to make the payment. To assure DW Trucks of payment, Express signed a one-year note with 6% interest per annum, to be payable at maturity. Express Company's year-end is on December 31. Prepare all the necessary journal entries related to the notes payable from the time it is signed to the maturity date.

Date	Account Title and Explanation	Debit	Credit

AP-7B (❻)

On August 1, 2016, DEBTS Bank agreed to lend Zirkula Enterprises $110,000. Zirkula signed a $110,000, 10-month, 12% note. Zirkula Enterprises has a year-end of December 31. Interest is payable at maturity.

Required

Prepare the journal entry for Zirkula Enterprises for the following.

a) On the date the note was signed

b) At year-end

c) On May 31, 2017, when the note is repaid

Date	Account Title and Explanation	Debit	Credit

AP-8B (❻)

On May 1, 2016, Cool Water signed a $50,000, six-month note payable with a 7% interest rate. Cool Water has a September 30 year-end.

Required

Prepare the necessary journal entries to record the following.

a) The signing of the note payable on May 1, 2016

b) The required adjusting entry on September 30, 2016

c) The payment of interest and repayment of the note on November 1, 2016

Date	Account Title and Explanation	Debit	Credit

AP-9B (⑥)

On November 1, 2016, Compression Company signed a $100,000, eight-month note payable with a 5% interest rate. Compression Company has a December 31 year-end.

Required

Prepare the necessary journal entries to record the following.

a)   The signing of the note payable on November 1, 2016

b)   The required adjusting entry on December 31, 2016

c)   The payment of interest and repayment of the note on July 1, 2017

Date	Account Title and Explanation	Debit	Credit

Analysis

The accounting practice of estimating and recording accrued expense is part of accrual-based accounting. This process is different from cash-based accounting, which is an accounting practice that records expenses and revenue only when cash is paid or received. What benefit does accrual-based accounting have over cash-based accounting?

_____

_____

_____

_____

_____

AP-10B (❺)

A local transit company sells transit passes for $150 each. The company sold 1,200 units on February 1, 2016, and each one is valid for six months.

Required

Write the entry for the following.

a) The sale of the transit passes

b) The entry to be recorded on June 30, the company's year-end

Date	Account Title and Explanation	Debit	Credit

AP-11B (❽)

Los Amigos Manufacturing builds and sells cars. On January 1, 2016, the company sold 150 cars for $30,000 each, on account. The cost to build each car is $7,000. Los Amigos does not automatically include warranties with the purchase of the car; however, the customer has the option to purchase the warranty separately. Los Amigos sold a four-year warranty for each car sold. Each warranty costs $2,000. Prepare the journal entries for the sale of the cars and warranties. Assume the cars were purchased on account and that the warranties were paid for in cash. Los Amigos uses a perpetual inventory system.

Date	Account Title and Explanation	Debit	Credit

AP-12B (❽)

PanPress Company sold four-year extended warranties on January 1, 2016 and received $300,000 cash. Record the journal entry related to unearned warranty revenue at the end of the first year, on December 31, 2016.

Date	Account Title and Explanation	Debit	Credit

AP-13B (❽)

SASA, a manufacturer of photocopying machines, offers customers a three-year warranty on the purchase of each machine. If a machine breaks down during this warranty period, SASA is required to repair or replace the machine. On the basis of historical experience, SASA determines that an average of $80 of parts per machine will be used for warranty obligations. SASA sold 300 machines during 2016. All journal entries related to warranties are recorded on December 31.

Required

a) Prepare the journal entry to record the estimated warranty liability for 2016.

b) Prepare the journal entry recorded in 2017 assuming SASA uses $5,000 in parts for warranty claims.

Date	Account Title and Explanation	Debit	Credit

c) How would the income statement be affected if SASA used $5,000 in parts in 2017 for warranty claims?

_____

_____

AP-14B (❽)

Solace produces and sells sunglasses and provides customers with a one-year warranty on all products. It is estimated that the company incurs approximately $10 of warranty expense on each pair sold. During 2016, the company sold 400 pairs of sunglasses. All journal entries related to warranties are recorded on December 31.

Required

a) Prepare a journal entry to record the estimated warranty liability.

b) During the year 2016, the company used $200 worth of inventory parts and paid $100 cash for staff salaries toward warranty claims. Prepare a journal entry to record this transaction.

Date	Account Title and Explanation	Debit	Credit

AP-15B (❼ ❽)

Spinicker sells in-home stereo systems. The corporation also sells a four-year warranty contract as a separate service. Spinicker sold 40,000 warranty contracts at $100 each in 2016. Spinicker recognizes warranty revenue evenly over the warranty period.

Required

a) Prepare a journal entry on December 31, 2016 to record the sale of the warranty contracts for the year.

Date	Account Title and Explanation	Debit	Credit

b) Explain how the unearned warranty revenue will appear on the balance sheet at the end of 2016.

_____

_____

c) Prepare the journal entry on December 31 to record warranty revenue in 2017.

Date	Account Title and Explanation	Debit	Credit

Analysis

Why do you think the businesses record the full amount of warranty expenses concurrently as products are sold even though the amount of warranty liabilities are reduced over the life of warranty period, which can be as long as several years?

_____

_____

_____

_____

_____

_____

_____

AP-16B (⑥)

On April 1, 2016, Sinister Toys signed a $600,000, six-month note payable with a 12% interest rate. Sinister Toys has a June 30 year-end.

Required

a) Record the signing of the note payable on April 1, 2016.

b) Prepare the required adjusting entry on June 30, 2016.

c) Record the payment of interest and repayment of the note on Oct 1, 2016.

Date	Account Title and Explanation	Debit	Credit

AP-17B (❷ ❺ ❻)

Shawn Clarity owns a consulting firm called Clarity Solutions. Clarity Solutions has a year-end of December 31. The firm had the following transactions during 2017.

Jan 1   Received $10,000 cash for consulting fees from a client. To date, $5,000 worth of services have been provided, and the rest will be provided on February 16.

Feb 16   Provided the services outstanding from the January 1 transaction.

Mar 11   Purchased office equipment worth $500, on account.

Apr 1   Purchased new office furniture for $7,000 from JJ Store by issuing a six-month note with 4% interest. Interest and principal payment is due at maturity.

May 11   Paid $500 cash for the purchase of equipment on March 11.

Jun 12   Received a $600 invoice for repair services, to be paid after 45 days.

Jul 27   Paid cash for the invoice received on June 12.

Sep 30   Recorded any payments and interest accrued related to the notes payable from April 1.

Oct 19   Received $2,000 cash from a client for consulting services provided.

Prepare journal entries to record the above transactions.

Date	Account Title and Explanation	Debit	Credit

AP-18B (❷ ❺ ❼)

During 2017, FitnessFirst Ltd. had the following transactions.

Feb 1   Borrowed a five-year loan for $150,000 with an interest rate of 5% per annum. Annual principal payment of $30,000 and interest is payable at the end of January.

Mar 1   Sold 100 three-month club membership to customers for a total $6,000 cash. Regardless of the number of times a customer visits the club, the monthly memberships are not refundable.

Mar 31   Recorded revenue earned from the March 1 transaction.

Apr 14   Purchased treadmills worth $20,000 from RunRun Company, on account.

Apr 30   Recorded revenue earned from the March 1 transaction.

May 25   Received utilities bill for $1,000, to be paid within 30 days.

May 31   Recorded revenue earned from the March 1 transaction.

Jun 14   Paid $10,000 cash to RunRun Company to reduce the balance owing.

Jun 24   Paid the utilities bill received on May 25.

Sep 1   Received $10,000 cash from customers for the sale of one-month memberships. Once the customer has paid the membership fees, it cannot be refunded.

Prepare journal entries to record the above transactions during 2017. FitnessFirst Ltd. has a year-end of December 31.

Date	Account Title and Explanation	Debit	Credit

Date	Account Title and Explanation	Debit	Credit

AP-19B (❹)

Tasty Cafe has recorded all its transactions for September 2017. As of September 30, the balance of the HST Payable account was $3,500 and the balance of the HST Recoverable account was $3,900.

Required

a) Will Tasty Cafe be remitting sales tax to the government, or will it receive a refund?

b) Prepare the journal entry that Tasty Cafe will prepare on September 30.

Date	Account Title and Explanation	Debit	Credit

AP-20B (❷ ❹)

Toy Retailer operates in a province where HST is applied at 13%. During August 2017, it had the following transactions.

Aug 12   Sold inventory to a customer for $2,000 plus HST for cash. The inventory costs $1,100.

Aug 15   Purchased inventory for $5,000 plus HST on account.

Record the transactions for August 2017.

Date	Account Title and Explanation	Debit	Credit

AP-21B (❽)

Safe Sound Airlines is a low-cost airline operating in North America. The company offers a customer loyalty program whereby customers are rewarded 1 "Safe Mile" for every 10 miles travelled with the airline. One Safe Mile can be redeemed for a two-cent discount toward future flights. In March 2016, customers flew 6,000,000 miles with Safe Sound Airlines. Historically, customers redeem an average of 55% of Safe Miles issued.

Required

a) Prepare the journal entry to record the issuance of Safe Miles in March 2016.

Date	Account Title and Explanation	Debit	Credit

b) Safe Sound Airlines' total air ticket sales in April was $640,000, of which $636,000 was received in cash and $4,000 was redeemed using Safe Miles. Prepare the journal entry to record the sales through cash and Safe Miles redemption in April.

Date	Account Title and Explanation	Debit	Credit

Analysis

If the redemption rate for the rewards program has decreased to 50% this year, should the company use the lower rate to record its redemption rewards liability?

_____

_____

_____

AP-22B (❼)

Brisbane Company has the following selected items and balance on its trial balance at its year-end on October 31, 2017.

Accounts Payable	$6,200
Accounts Receivable	8,700
Cash	9,200
Current Portion of Bank Loan	15,000
Estimated Warranty Liability	6,700
Inventory	32,400
Non-Current Portion of Bank Loan	80,000
Prepaid Insurance	2,600
Salaries Payable	5,400
Unearned Revenue	4,700

Required

a) Prepare the current liabilities portion of the balance sheet.

b) Based on the information available, calculate the current ratio and comment on the
    liquidity of the company.

_____

_____

_____

_____

_____

Analysis

A company is offered a discount of 2% if payment of a $100,000 invoice is made within 30
days of the invoice date. However the company realized that it would not have sufficient
funds until 59 days after the invoice date. The company has an operating line of credit
arranged with its bank for $1,000,000 at an annual interest rate of 5% on any outstanding
balance at the beginning of each month. Should the company borrow from its operating line
of credit to pay off the amount to its supplier and receive the discount?

_____

_____

_____

_____

_____

_____

_____

_____

_____

_____

_____

_____

Case Study

CS-1 (❷ ❸ ❹ ❺ ❻ ❼ ❽)

Fulton Electronics sells televisions and other electronics. All the electronics come with a default one-year warranty against defects. Warranty estimates are recorded every month. Fulton estimates that warranty repairs or replacements are 2% of the sales price. Customers are also able to purchase a two-year extended warranty. The warranty revenue is spread evenly over the two-year period. During September 2016, the following transactions occurred. The company uses the perpetual inventory system and operates in a province that has an HST rate of 13%.

Sep 1 Purchased store fixtures for $300,000 plus HST. Since Fulton does not have the cash, it signed a three-year note payable with a rate of 5%. Payment of $50,000 plus interest is due each March 1 and September 1 until the note matures.

Sep 1 Sold extended two-year warranties on products sold last month. Received $4,800 cash.

Sep 10 Incurred warranty costs of $500 to replace defective products sold last month. The warranty costs were taken from inventory.

Sep 14 Prepared the payroll for employees for first half of the month. The actual payment will be made at a later date. The employer also pays 100% of the CPP and 140% of EI. Details of the payroll are shown below.

Gross Pay	$5,000
Canada Pension Plan	$247
Employment Insurance	$94
Income Tax	$1,000

Sep 15 Cash sales for the first half of the month amount to $400,000 plus HST. Cost of goods sold is $240,000. Estimated warranty costs must also be recorded. There is no sales tax recorded on warranty estimates.

Sep 15 Paid the amount of payroll owing to employees from September 14.

Sep 20 Purchased inventory on account for $150,000 plus HST.

Sep 29 Prepared the payroll for employees for the second half of the month. The actual payment will be made at a later date. The employer also pays 100% of the CPP and 140% of EI. Details of the payroll are shown below.

Gross Pay	$6,000
Canada Pension Plan	$297
Employment Insurance	$113
Income Tax	$1,200

Sep 30   Sales for the second half of the month amount to $350,000 plus HST. Cost of goods sold is $210,000. Estimated warranty costs must also be recorded. There is no sales tax recorded on warranty estimates.

Sep 30   Paid the amounts of payroll owing to employees from September 29.

Sep 30   Paid the HST owing for the month of September.

Sep 30   Paid the payroll remittance to the CRA for the amount owing from payroll for the month of September.

Sep 30   Accrued one month of interest on the note payable from September 1.

Sep 30   Earned one month of extended warranty revenue from September 1.

Required

a)   Complete journal entries for the above transactions for the month of September 2016.

Date	Account Title and Explanation	Debit	Credit

Date	Account Title and Explanation	Debit	Credit

Date	Account Title and Explanation	Debit	Credit

b) How will the liabilities be reported as current or non-current on the balance sheet on September 30, 2016?

_____

_____

_____

_____

_____

_____

_____

_____

_____

_____

_____

_____

_____

_____

_____

_____

_____

_____

_____

_____

_____

_____

Critical Thinking

CT-1 (8)

Contingent liabilities arise when the payment of a liability depends on uncertain future events, such as the result of a lawsuit.

Current accounting practice requires that when the payment for a contingent liability is probable, and the amount can be reasonably estimated, the amount must be accrued on the balance sheet.

Is this practice reasonable, (in light of the fact that the liability is not definite and only estimates are used)? Does this practice mislead owners regarding the actual state of affairs surrounding liabilities? Discuss.

Chapter 5

PARTNERSHIPS

❶ Describe the charactcristics, advantages and disadvantages of a partnership

❷ Describe different types of partnerships

❸ Record the formation of a partnership

❹ Record the division of income or loss

❺ Record partners' drawings

❻ Prepare financial statements for a partnership

❼ Account for the addition or withdrawal of a partner

❽ Record the liquidation of a partnership

AMEENGAGE™ Access **ameengage.com** for integrated resources including tutorials, practice exercises, the digital textbook and more.

Assessment Questions

AS-1 (❶)

What is a partnership?

_____

_____

_____

_____

_____

_____

_____

_____

_____

_____

AS-2 (❶)

Compare and contrast the characteristics of proprietorships and partnerships.

Characteristic	Proprietorship	Partnership
Amount of capital that can be raised		
Control		
Dissolution		
Liability		
Number of owners		
Profits		
Set Up		
Skills		
Taxation		

AS-3 (❹)

List different ways in which partnership profits may be divided.

_____

_____

_____

_____

_____

_____

AS-4 (❶)

List two advantages of organizing a business as a partnership over a proprietorship.

_____

_____

_____

_____

AS-5 (❸)

What is a partnership agreement?

_____

_____

_____

_____

AS-6 (❸)

What methods may partners choose to pay themselves, other than straight division of profits?

_____

_____

_____

_____

_____

_____

_____

_____

AS-7 (❹)

Explain the closing of the income summary account for partnerships.

_____

_____

_____

_____

_____

AS-8 (❺)

During the year, partners may withdraw cash or other assets. What account is used to accumulate these withdrawals?

_____

_____

_____

_____

_____

_____

AS-9 (❺)

What happens to partners' drawings at year-end?

_____

_____

_____

_____

_____

_____

_____

AS-10 (❼)

When a partner is added or removed from the partnership, what happens to the partnership agreement?

_____

_____

_____

AS-11 (❼)

What are the two different ways withdrawal of a partner can take place?

_____

_____

_____

AS-12 (❽)

In liquidating a partnership, what happens if assets are sold for amounts other than their book values?

_____

_____

_____

_____

_____

_____

Application Questions Group A

AP-1A (❸)

Chandra Heesch and Allie Owenby have decided to form a partnership on January 1, 2016. Each partner has agreed to contribute $10,000. Write the journal entry to record the formation of the partnership.

Date	Account Title and Explanation	Debit	Credit

AP-2A (❸)

On May 1, 2016, Nataliya, Sam and Seechi form a partnership and open a small convenience store. All the partners invest $10,000 cash, and Nataliya also invests equipment worth $5,000.

Required

a) Calculate the total contribution of each partner.

	Nataliya	Sam	Seechi

b) Prepare a journal entry to set up the partnership, and to record the additional investment.

Date	Account Title and Explanation	Debit	Credit

AP-3A (❸)

The following four people started a partnership and brought the assets and liabilities listed into the new business.

Biyanka Lee	
Cash	$14,000
Accounts Receivable	5,000
Allowance for Doubtful Accounts	800
Note Payable	2,500

Bob Fire	
Cash	$55,000
Equipment	11,000
Accumulated Depreciation	1,000
Bank Loan	8,000

Larry Ding	
Cash	$28,000
Building	240,000

Freeda Red	
Cash	$60,000

Note: An independent appraiser determined that the allowance for doubtful accounts should be $600. All other assets are recorded at their fair market values.

Required

a) When the partnership is formed, show the account balances that will be listed in the company's books.

ACCOUNTS	Debit	Credit
Cash		
Accounts Receivable		
Allowance for Doubtful Accounts		
Equipment		
Accumulated Depreciation		
Building		
Bank Loan		
Note Payable		
Biyanka Lee, Capital		
Bob Fire, Capital		
Larry Ding, Capital		
Freeda Red, Capital		
Total		

b) Earnings are equally divided among the partners. During 2016, the company earned a net income of $360,000. Prepare a journal entry on December 31, 2016 to close the income summary account at year-end.

Date	Account Title and Explanation	Debit	Credit

c) Independent of part b), suppose it was decided that Biyanka Lee will receive 10%, Bob Fire will receive 25%, Larry Ding will receive 40%, and Freeda Red will receive 25% of the profits. During 2016, the company had a net loss of $15,000. Prepare the journal entry on December 31, 2016 to close the income summary account at year-end.

Date	Account Title and Explanation	Debit	Credit

d) Independent of parts b) and c), suppose it was decided that the earnings will be divided based on each partner's capital contribution. During 2016, the company earned a net income of $86,000. Prepare the journal entry on December 31, 2016 to close the income summary account at year-end.

Date	Account Title and Explanation	Debit	Credit

AP-4A (❹)

Mallory Longshore, Lakisha Laffey and Avis Hemsley set up a partnership at the beginning of 2016. Mallory contributed $10,000 in cash. Lakisha contributed a van worth $20,000. Avis contributed equipment worth $15,000. The partnership made $9,000 net income for the year. According to the partnership agreement, profits are divided in the ratio of their initial contributions.

Required

a) Record the entry for the division of the profit on December 31, 2016. Assume that revenues and expenses have already been closed to the income summary account.

Date	Account Title and Explanation	Debit	Credit

b) Assume that the partnership recorded a loss of $4,500. Record the entry for the division of the loss. Assume that revenues and expenses have already been closed to the income summary account.

Date	Account Title and Explanation	Debit	Credit

AP-5A (❹)

Brian, Miley and Adriana operate a business under partnership. It was decided that Brian, Miley and Adriana will receive a salary of $65,000, $70,000 and $55,000 respectively. The remaining profit will be equally divided among the partners. During the year 2016, the company made a net income of $160,000. Calculate the amount of net income each partner will receive.

	Total	Brian	Miley	Adriana

AP-6A (❹)

A. Anna, P. Peter and J. Jackson formed a partnership in 2015. In 2017, the beginning capital balance of each partner was $25,000, $35,000 and $30,000 respectively. During 2017, the company earned a net income of $63,000, and A. Anna withdrew $25,000 while P. Peter and J. Jackson withdrew $40,000 and $35,000 respectively.

Required

a) Calculate the amount of net income each partner will receive based on the following independent scenarios.

(i)   the earnings are divided equally

(ii) A. Anna receives 30%, P. Peter receives 40%, and J. Jackson receives 30% of the earnings

(iii) the earnings are divided based on the partner's capital balance at the beginning of the year

	(i)	(ii)	(iii)
A. Anna			
P. Peter			
J. Jackson			

b) Calculate the ending capital balance of each partner, assuming that method (ii) is used to divide earnings.

	A. Anna	P. Peter	J. Jackson
Beginning Capital Balance			
Add: Additional Contribution			
Share of Net Income			
Subtotal			
Less: Drawings			
Ending Capital Balance			

c) A. Anna, P. Peter and J. Jackson decide to receive a salary of $40,000, $55,000 and $45,000 respectively. The remaining earnings will be divided among each partner equally. During 2018, the company earned a net income of $149,000. Calculate the amount of net income that each partner will receive.

	Total	A. Anna	P. Peter	J. Jackson
Net Income				
Salary				
Remainder				
Total Share				

d) During 2018, A. Anna, P. Peter and J. Jackson withdrew $10,000, $15,000 and $12,000 respectively. Prepare the journal entries to record the drawings.

Date	Account Title and Explanation	Debit	Credit

e) Calculate the ending capital balance of each partner. The beginning balance for 2018 is the ending value calculated in part b).

_____

_____

_____

_____

_____

AP-7A (③ ④ ⑤ ⑥ ⑦)

On January 1, 2016, Bob, Mike and Amy form a partnership to start a small public accounting firm. Bob, Mike and Amy have invested $64,000, $55,000 and $80,000 respectively. Mike has also invested a piece of equipment worth $2,000. During the first year of operations in 2016, the firm earned a net income of $280,000. All earnings are to be divided according to the initial capital contribution of each partner. In addition, Bob and Amy withdrew $5,000 and $7,000 cash from the business. During the second year of operations on January 1, 2017, a new partner (Mia) was added to the firm. Mia purchased 80% of Amy's investment and 10% of Mike's investment (equity) in the business.

Required

a) Assuming year-end is on December 31, prepare the journal entries to set up the partnership, record the drawings and distribute the income for 2016. Also, prepare any additional closing or adjusting entries.

Date	Account Title and Explanation	Debit	Credit

b) Prepare the journal entry to record the admission of Mia.

Date	Account Title and Explanation	Debit	Credit

c) Calculate the ending capital balance of each partner after the addition of Mia on January 1, 2017.

	Bob	Mike	Amy	Mia

AP-8A (❼)

Sylvia, Sonia and Sana are all partners who operate a beauty salon called S3 Beauty. On January 1, 2016, Sylvia, Sonia and Sana had a capital balance of $320,000, $215,000 and $360,000 respectively. Due to the successful growth of the business, the original partners have agreed to add an additional partner, Sharon. Sharon will be investing $300,000 cash in the business.

Required

a) Calculate the new capital balance for each partner after Sharon has been added to the partnership.

	Sylvia	Sonia	Sana	Sharon	Total

b) Prepare the journal entry to record the admission of Sharon from part a).

Date	Account Title and Explanation	Debit	Credit

c) Consider this independent scenario. S3 Beauty has made a good reputation for itself in the market and has a large base of loyal customers. Since the company has a higher market value, Sharon has agreed to invest $390,000 into the business and receive a $300,000 share of the business' book value. Any difference is split equally among the original partners. Calculate the new capital balance for each partner after Sharon has been added to the partnership.

	Sylvia	Sonia	Sana	Sharon	Total

d) Prepare the journal entry to record the admission of Sharon from part c).

Date	Account Title and Explanation	Debit	Credit

e) Consider this independent scenario. S3 Beauty has made a good reputation for itself in the market and has a large base of loyal customers. Since a partnership with Sharon will be very beneficial for S3 Beauty, S3 Beauty will provide Sharon with a $300,000 share of the business' book value for a $285,000 investment. Any difference is split equally among the original partners. Calculate the new capital balance for each partner after Sharon has been added to the partnership.

	Sylvia	Sonia	Sana	Sharon	Total

f)   Prepare the journal entry to record the admission of Sharon from part e).

Date	Account Title and Explanation	Debit	Credit

Analysis

Whenever an admission or withdrawal takes place in a partnership, is it necessary to change the name of the partnership to reflect the changes? Explain.

_____

_____

_____

_____

AP-9A (❺)

Tanisha Vanscyoc and Kurt Vicini operate a partnership that produces custom-made furniture. On April 12, 2016, Tanisha withdrew $50,000 in cash. On April 15, Kurt removed a sofa and chairs worth $30,000 for use in his own home.

Required

a)   Write the journal entry to record these transactions.

Date	Account Title and Explanation	Debit	Credit

b) Write the journal entry to close the Drawings accounts on December 31, 2016.

Date	Account Title and Explanation	Debit	Credit

AP-10A (❽)

Patricia, Karla, and Nathan operate a small law firm under a partnership. However, due to some internal conflicts, all the partners have agreed to end the partnership. The following items remain in the balance sheet on June 30, 2016 after all the assets have been liquidated.

Cash	$450,000
Capital—Patricia	188,000
Capital—Karla	82,000
Capital—Nathan	210,000

Prepare the journal entries to allocate any profit or loss on sale of assets, and to record cash distribution.

Date	Account Title and Explanation	Debit	Credit

AP-11A (⑧)

Twenty years ago, three brothers formed a partnership, which now has to end due to their increasing conflicts. Before the liquidation, the partnership had assets valued at $500,000 and liabilities valued at $300,000. The partners' equity balances were $50,000 for Brother A, $70,000 for Brother B and $80,000 for Brother C. The brothers sold the net assets for $230,000. Note that any profit or loss is distributed equally among the partners according to the terms of their partnership agreement. Prepare journal entries on December 31, 2016 for the following items.

- The sale of net assets.
- The allocation of the gain or loss on the sale of net assets.
- The cash distribution to the three brothers.

Date	Account Title and Explanation	Debit	Credit

AP-12A (❼)

Thomas, Helen, and Ahmed formed a partnership in 2016 to make furniture for commercial projects. On January 1, 2017, the partners had the following capital account balances: Thomas—$25,000, Helen—$35,000 and Ahmed—$50,000. On January 1, 2017 Helen decided to withdraw from the partnership. Helen sold 40% of her portion of capital to Thomas and the remaining 60% to Ahmed. Prepare a journal entry to record the transaction and calculate the balance of the partners' capital accounts after the withdrawal of Helen.

Date	Account Title and Explanation	Debit	Credit

	Thomas	Helen	Ahmed	Total
Capital balance before withdrawal				
Withdrawal of Helen				
Capital balance after withdrawal				

Application Questions Group B

AP-1B (❸)

Ted Coverdale and Julio Kadlec set up a new partnership on March 10, 2016. Ted contributes a warehouse and land worth a combined $1,000,000. Market value of the warehouse is $300,000. Julio contributes $1,000,000 in cash. Write the journal entry to record the contributions to the partnership.

Date	Account Title and Explanation	Debit	Credit

AP-2B (❶ ❸)

Andrew Watson and Baker Ford formed a partnership on January 1, 2016 to supply bottled water to businesses. Andrew contributed $10,000 cash and a vehicle with a book value $6,000. Baker brought $6,000 cash and equipment with a book value $10,000. An independent appraiser determined that the vehicle is valued at $5,500 and the equipment is valued at $8,800.

Required

a) Prepare a journal entry to record formation of the business.

Date	Account Title and Explanation	Debit	Credit

b) On May 1, 2016, Baker invested an additional $4,000 in cash into the business. Record the journal entry.

Date	Account Title and Explanation	Debit	Credit

Analysis

What are some of the advantages of Andrew and Baker forming a partnership?

_____

_____

_____

_____

AP-3B (❹)

Selena Hegarty, Cody Debruyn and Lenore Raap operate their business as a partnership. According to their partnership agreement, Selena and Lenore split 51% of the profits equally. The remainder of the profits goes to Cody. Record the entry for the division of profits of $100,000 on December 31, 2016. Assume that revenues and expenses have already been closed to the income summary account.

Date	Account Title and Explanation	Debit	Credit

Analysis

Selena is not happy about how the profit is allocated. She is working twice as much as the other partners. What can the other partners do to resolve this issue?

_____

_____

AP-4B (❹)

Noemi Loop, Lilia Hopkin and Guy Scoggin perform in a band operating as a partnership. According to the partnership agreement, Noemi receives a salary of $22,000, Lilia receives a salary of $30,000, and Guy receives a salary of $28,000. They are also to receive nominal interest of 5% on the capital at the end of the preceding year (Noemi's capital—$1,000, Lilia's capital—$10,000, Guy's capital—$20,000). The remainder is divided equally. During the year the partners withdrew $22,000 each as an advance to their share of partnership earnings. The band made $100,000 after paying all other expenses.

Required

a) Prepare a schedule showing changes in the partners' capital during the year.

_____

_____

_____

_____

_____

_____

_____

_____

_____

_____

_____

b) Assume that the net income remaining is distributed on the ratio of the opening balance of capital. Prepare the schedule showing the changes in capital.

_____

_____

_____

_____

_____

_____

_____

_____

_____

c) Based on the division of profits calculated in part b), prepare the journal entry to record the distribution of profits and close the drawings accounts on December 31. Assume that revenues and expenses have already been closed to the income summary account.

Date	Account Title and Explanation	Debit	Credit

AP-5B (❹)

Mathew, Henry and Tom formed a partnership to open a grocery store in 2016. Each partner contributed $30,000 cash. In addition, Henry brought some furniture worth $3,000 and Tom brought a vehicle worth $8,000. An independent appraiser determined the vehicle should be valued at $7,000.

Required

a) During 2016, the business earned a net income of $90,000. The partners decided to divide profit equally. Prepare a journal entry to close the income summary account at year-end.

Date	Account Title and Explanation	Debit	Credit

b) Assume instead that Mathew will receive 25% of the profit, Henry will receive 30% of the profit and Tom will receive 45% of the profit. During the year the business made a loss of $30,000. Prepare a journal entry to close the income summary account at year-end.

Date	Account Title and Explanation	Debit	Credit

c) Assume instead that profits will be divided based on each partner's capital contribution. During the year, the business made a net income of $60,000. Prepare a journal entry to close the income summary account at year-end.

Date	Account Title and Explanation	Debit	Credit

AP-6B (❹)

Chloe, Chen and Yang are in partnership. According to the partnership agreement, Chloe and Chen will receive a salary of $5,000 each. Each partner will also be entitled to receive 3% interest on their capital account balance at the beginning of the year. Any profit and losses are to be shared in the ratio 3:2:1 to Chloe, Chen and Yang, respectively. Capital account balances are Chloe—$25,000, Chen—$20,000 and Yang—$10,000. During 2016, the business earned a net income of $65,000. Calculate the amount of net income each partner will receive.

	Total	Chloe	Chen	Yang

AP-7B (❸ ❹ ❺ ❻ ❼)

The following table shows the summary of amounts contributed by each partner to a new partnership called Dev, Patel and Forbes on January 1, 2016.

Karthik Dev

Cash	$20,000
Accounts Receivable	5,000
Allowance for Doubtful Accounts	900
Note Payable	3,000

Harish Patel

Cash	$15,000
Bank Loan	6,000
Equipment	9,000
Accumulated Depreciation	1,000

John Forbes

Cash	$18,000
Building	100,000
Vehicle	15,000
Accumulated Depreciation	3,000

An independent appraiser determined the following values for some of the items. All other items are listed at their fair market value.

- Allowance for doubtful accounts should be $1,500
- Equipment should be $10,000
- Vehicle should be $6,000

Required

a) Prepare a trial balance with the account balances.

Accounts	Debit	Credit

b) During 2016 the business earned a net income of $150,000. Karthik, Harish and John withdraw $10,000, $8,000, and $15,000 respectively. Karthik and Harish are entitled to a salary of $10,000 each. Partners are also entitled to receive 5% interest on capital (beginning balance). Remaining earnings are divided among the partners in the ratio 1:4:5 to Karthik, Harish and John, respectively. Prepare a statement showing division of profits.

	Total	Karthik	Harish	John

c) Prepare a statement of changes in partners' equity.

	John	Karthik	Harish	Total

d) On January 1, 2017, Karthik decided to withdraw from the partnership. Harish and John have decided to buy out Karthik's interest in equal portion. Prepare the journal entry to record the transaction and calculate the balance of the partners' capital accounts after Karthik leaves.

Date	Account Title and Explanation	Debit	Credit

	John	Karthik	Harish	Total
Capital balance before withdrawal				
Withdrawal of Karthik				
Capital balance after withdrawal				

e) Independent of part d), assume instead that the partners have decided to pay off Karthik using partnership assets. Prepare the journal entry to record the transaction and calculate the balance of partners' capital accounts after Karthik leaves.

Date	Account Title and Explanation	Debit	Credit

	John	Karthik	Harish	Total
Capital balance before withdrawal				
Withdrawal of Karthik				
Capital balance after withdrawal				

Analysis

Compare the impact on the assets of the partnership in parts d) and e).

_____

_____

_____

_____

AP-8B (❼)

Jack, John, and Joe have been operating a business as a partnership for several years. On January 1, 2016, Jack, John and Joe had a capital balance of $255,000, $180,000 and $132,000 respectively. However, due to a business conflict, Joe decided to withdraw from the partnership. Jack and John decided to pay off Joe using the partnership's cash.

Required

a) Calculate the new capital balance for each partner after the withdrawal of Joe.

	Jack	John	Joe	Total

b) Prepare the journal entry to record the withdrawal of Joe.

Date	Account Title and Explanation	Debit	Credit

c) After Joe has left, Jack and John added Jim to the partnership on January 1, 2016. A partnership with Jim will considerably increase the value of the business. Therefore, Jim receives a $100,000 share of the business' book value for an $80,000 investment. Calculate the new capital balance for each partner after Joe has been withdrawn and Jim has been added to the partnership.

	Jack	John	Jim	Total

d) Prepare the journal entry to record the admission of Jim from part c).

Date	Account Title and Explanation	Debit	Credit

e) Independent of part c), assume that Jim will receive a $100,000 share of the business' book value for a $130,000 investment. Calculate the new capital balance for each partner after Joe has been withdrawn and Jim has been added to the partnership.

	Jack	John	Jim	Total

f) Prepare the journal entry to record the admission of Jim from part e).

Date	Account Title and Explanation	Debit	Credit

g) Independent of part a), assume that when Joe leaves, Joe is going to sell his portion of the partnership to Jim. Jim is also going to purchase 20% of Jack's share in the partnership. The cash transaction will be a private matter between Jim and the two partners; however, the capital amounts must be transferred to Jim in the partnership records. Calculate the new capital balances for each partner

	Jack	John	Joe	Jim	Total

h) Prepare the journal entry to record the admission of Jim and the withdrawal of Joe from part g).

Date	Account Title and Explanation	Debit	Credit

AP-9B (❺)

Bryan Butryn and Jason Barfoot are in a partnership selling mobile phones. On May 1, 2016, Jason took a mobile phone worth $800 from the business for his personal use. On December 31, 2016, Bryan withdrew $5,000 cash and Jason withdrew $3,000 cash for personal use.

Required

a) Write the journal entries to record the withdrawal transactions.

Date	Account Title and Explanation	Debit	Credit

b) Write journal entry to close the drawings account on December 31, 2016.

Date	Account Title and Explanation	Debit	Credit

AP-10B (❽)

LIN Partnership has to be terminated due to the death of one of the partners. After the liquidation, the following items remained in the balance sheet.

LIN Partnership Balance Sheet As at March 31, 2016	
Cash	**$150,000**
Partners' Equity	
Partner A	30,000
Partner B	55,000
Partner C	20,000
Partner D	45,000
Total	**$150,000**

Prepare the journal entries to record cash distribution. Assume that the assets were sold at their book value.

Date	Account Title and Explanation	Debit	Credit

AP-11B (⑧)

Chong partnership was terminated on December 31, 2016 due to a dispute between partners. Before liquidation the total assets were valued at $600,000 and total liabilities were valued at $250,000. The partners' equity balances were as follows: Partner X—$60,000, Partner Y—$90,000 and Partner Z—$200,000. Net assets were sold for $320,000. The partnership agreement states profit and losses are to be shared in the ratio 2:3:3 between Partner X, Y and Z respectively. Prepare the journal entries to record the liquidation of the business.

Date	Account Title and Explanation	Debit	Credit

Analysis

What are the reasons a partnership would decide to liquidate?

_____

_____

_____

_____

_____

_____

_____

_____

_____

_____

AP-12B (❼)

Cooper, Amy and Jacob formed a partnership in 2016. On January 1, 2017, the partners had the following capital account balances: Cooper—$35,000, Amy—$60,000 and Jacob—$50,000. On January 1, 2017, Jacob decided to withdraw from the partnership due to unresolved disputes. The withdrawal of Jacob was paid from the partnership's assets. Prepare the journal entry to record the transaction and calculate the balance of the partners' capital accounts after the withdrawal of Jacob.

Date	Account Title and Explanation	Debit	Credit

	Cooper	Amy	Jacob	Total
Capital balance before withdrawal				
Withdrawal of Jacob				
Capital balance after withdrawal				

Case Study

CS-1 (❹ ❺ ❻)

For the year ended December 31, 2016, a partnership had sales of $500,000 and expenses of $400,000 before allocation of partners' salaries, interest on capital and charges for equipment.

There are two partners who own the business. Each partner will receive earnings based on four factors. Each partner will receive a salary of $40,000. Each partner will receive interest on capital contributions which amounts to $2,000 for Partner A, and $1,000 for Partner B. Partner B brought equipment into the business and receives $2,000 "rent" on the equipment each year. Remaining profits are divided equally. The opening balances of capital were $200,000 for Partner A and $100,000 for Partner B.

During the year, the partners withdrew $30,000 as advances on their yearly salary.

Required

a) Calculate the net income of the partnership.

_____

_____

_____

_____

_____

_____

_____

b) Show the calculation of the share of income to be distributed to each partner.

_____

_____

_____

_____

_____

_____

_____

c) Prepare journal entries to record the distribution of income, drawings and closing entries.

Date	Account Title and Explanation	Debit	Credit

d) Explain why salaries, interest and rental of equipment are not included in the closing entries.

_____

_____

_____

_____

_____

_____

_____

_____

_____

_____

_____

_____

e) Prepare the statement of partners' equity for the year ended December 31, 2016.

Critical Thinking

CT-1 (❶ ❷)

Sometimes a person simply wants to invest in a business as an owner, rather than actively participate in the business. This is simple when the business is organized as a corporation. By definition, a proprietorship has only one owner. If the investor participates in a partnership, the investor assumes unlimited liability for the partnership.

Required

a) Is it wise to invest in a partnership if one does not want to actively participate in the partnership?

_____

_____

_____

_____

_____

_____

_____

_____

_____

_____

b) Are there any steps an investor could take to limit his liability? Discuss.

_____

_____

_____

_____

_____

_____

Chapter 6

CORPORATIONS: CONTRIBUTED CAPITAL AND DIVIDENDS

LEARNING OUTCOMES

❶ Describe the characteristics of corporate organizations

❷ Describe differences between public and private corporations

❸ Explain shareholders' equity

❹ Record the issuance of shares

❺ Record the payment of cash dividends

❻ Record stock splits and stock dividends

❼ Record income tax expense

❽ Record the closing entries for a corporation

❾ Calculate retained earnings

❿ Explain the importance of ethics for corporate reporting

Appendix

⓫ Record the reacquisition of shares

AMEENGAGE™ *Access **ameengage.com** for integrated resources including tutorials, practice exercises, the digital textbook and more.*

Assessment Questions

AS-1 (❶)

What is a common term that is used to call an owner of a corporation?

_____

_____

AS-2 (❶)

Why is tax paid twice on earnings from a corporation? What is this phenomenon called?

_____

_____

_____

_____

_____

AS-3 (❶)

List four advantages and two disadvantages of the corporate form of ownership.

Advantages

_____

_____

_____

_____

_____

_____

_____

_____

_____

Disadvantages

_____

_____

_____

_____

_____

_____

_____

_____

_____

_____

_____

_____

AS-3 (❶)

AS-4 (❶)

What is a not-for-profit corporation? How is it different from a for-profit corporation?

AS-5 (❷)

Explain the main difference between a public corporation and a private corporation.

AS-6 (❷)

From which two accounting standards can a private corporation choose?

AS-7 (❷)

Why might a private corporation choose to adopt ASPE over IFRS?

AS-8 (❷)

What are some reasons why a private enterprise would adopt IFRS over ASPE?

_____

_____

_____

_____

_____

AS-9 (❸)

Which portion of shareholders' equity relates to contributions by shareholders? Which relates to accumulated earnings?

_____

_____

_____

_____

AS-10 (❸)

Name the two sub-categories of contributed capital.

_____

_____

_____

AS-11 (❸)

You are preparing the financial statements for a corporation. You must disclose the number of shares authorized. Where would you find the number of shares authorized?

_____

_____

_____

AS-12 (❸)

What is meant by "outstanding shares"?

_____

_____

_____

AS-13 (❸)

Define "retained earnings."

_____

_____

_____

AS-14 (❹)

What may shares be issued for?

_____

_____

AS-15 (❸)

What are some differences between common shareholders and preferred shareholders?

_____

_____

_____

_____

_____

_____

_____

AS-16 (❸)

List some characteristics of common shares.

_____

_____

_____

_____

_____

_____

_____

_____

AS-17 (❸)

List some characteristics of preferred shares.

_____

_____

_____

_____

_____

_____

_____

_____

_____

_____

_____

_____

AS-18 (❸)

Which feature of preferred shares gives shareholders the right to receive dividends in arrears?

AS-19 (❸)

Explain the difference between no-par value shares and par value shares. How are no-par value shares valued at issuing?

AS-20 (❹)

When shares of a corporation are issued in exchange for assets or services, how are the shares valued in the corporation's books?

AS-21 (❺)

List and describe the three dates associated with accounting for dividends.

_____

_____

_____

_____

_____

_____

_____

AS-22 (❺ ❻)

Who decides the amount of a dividend to be paid to shareholders?

_____

_____

_____

_____

AS-23 (❹)

What are the two methods of accounting for share issue costs?

_____

_____

_____

_____

_____

_____

_____

AS-24 (❶)

What does it mean when a corporation is considered a going concern?

_____

_____

_____

_____

_____

AS-25 (❻)

Explain a stock split and a reverse stock split.

_____

_____

_____

_____

_____

AS-26 (❶)

Provide a few possible reasons why a company may want to reacquire its shares.

_____

_____

_____

_____

_____

_____

_____

AS-27 (◐)

What effect does a share reacquisition transaction have on a company's assets, liabilities and shareholders' equity?

_____

_____

_____

_____

_____

_____

_____

AS-28 (◐)

Describe the contributed surplus account. Provide an example of a situation that causes the contributed surplus account balance to increase.

_____

_____

_____

_____

_____

_____

_____

_____

_____

_____

_____

---------- **Application Questions Group A** ----------

AP-1A (❼)

At year-end on December 31, 2016, Shuster Home Decor Inc. has accounting income (before income tax expense calculation) of $102,000. Write the journal entry to record the income tax expense. Assume the tax rate is 30%.

Date	Account Title and Explanation	Debit	Credit

AP-2A (❽)

An extract from MC Consulting's pre-closing trial balance for the year ended December 31, 2016 is shown below. The company's net income for the year was $82,000.

MC Consulting Trial Balance (Extract) December 31, 2016		
Account Title	**Debit**	**Credit**
Sales Revenue		240,000
Cost of Goods Sold	85,000	
Salaries Expense	30,000	
Rent Expense	10,000	
Income Tax Expense	13,000	

Prepare the closing entries for MC Consulting assuming the company uses the income summary account.

Date	Account Title and Explanation	Debit	Credit

AP-3A (❺)

On February 1, 2016, Adam Enterprises declares a dividend of $4,800 to common shareholders to be paid on February 4. Record the journal entry associated with this transaction.

Date	Account Title and Explanation	Debit	Credit

AP-4A (❸)

The shareholders' equity of Thomas Inc. at March 31, 2016 is shown below.

Additional Information
- The preferred shares have an average issue price of $5.00 per share.
- The common shares have an average issue price of $3.00 per share.

Fill in the grey areas in the table below with the correct numbers.

Thomas Inc. Shareholders' Equity As at March 31, 2016	
Share Capital	
Preferred Shares, 280,000 shares authorized, 23,000 shares issued and outstanding	
Common Shares, unlimited shares authorized, 120,000 shares issued and outstanding	
Total Share Capital	475,000
Retained Earnings	
Total Shareholders' Equity	$533,675

Analysis

A corporation has the choice to issue only common shares or issue mainly preferred shares. (All corporations must have at least one class of common shares outstanding). If you were a director on the board of a newly Incorporated, fast-growing corporation, which is planning to issue shares to the general public, what type of shares would you suggest the management to issue?

_____

_____

_____

_____

_____

_____

_____

_____

_____

AP-5A (❹)

Earnestine, Kepplinger & Co. began a new public corporation. During the first month of operations, it had the following share transactions.

Required

a) Earnestine, Kepplinger & Co. issued 10,000 common shares for $100,000 on May 1, 2016. Write the journal entry to record the transaction.

Date	Account Title and Explanation	Debit	Credit

b) On May 1, 2016, Earnestine, Kepplinger & Co. issued an additional 10,000 common shares in exchange for land and a building. The land was valued at $60,000 and the building was valued at $50,000. Record the transaction.

Date	Account Title and Explanation	Debit	Credit

c) The lawyer that handled the issue of shares has sent a bill for $5,000. The lawyer has agreed to accept 500 common shares instead of cash. Record the transaction on May 10, 2016.

Date	Account Title and Explanation	Debit	Credit

Analysis

In the case of non-monetary exchanges of assets and services for issued shares, a corporation can choose to evaluate the fair value of shares issued with two options.

Option 1: Fair value of assets or services received
Option 2: Fair value of the shares issued

Think of a scenario when option 1 is preferred over option 2 by accountants and explain why.

_____

_____

_____

_____

_____

_____

_____

_____

AP-6A (❹)

Swanson Inc. was formed on January 1, 2016 and issued 10,000 common shares for $2 per share on that date. During the year the following additional share transactions occurred.

May 15   Issued 4,500 common shares for $2.75 per share.

Jul 1   Issued 5,000 common shares in exchange for equipment with a fair value of $14,500.

Sep 26   Issued 2,800 common shares for $2.50 per share.

Required

a) Prepare the journal entries to record the above transactions (including the entry to record the formation of Swanson Inc.).

Date	Account Title and Explanation	Debit	Credit

b) Determine the total number and value of common shares issued and outstanding as at December 31, 2016 by completing the following table.

Date	# of shares issued	$ per share	Total ($)
Jan 1	10,000	$2.00	
May 15	4,500	$2.75	
Jul 1	5,000		$14,500
Sep 26	2,800	$2.50	
Total Dec 31, 2016			

Analysis

Suppose that Joe, the president of Swanson Inc., owns 14,500 of the outstanding shares. What percentage ownership does Joe have?

_____

_____

_____

AP-7A (5)

a) On July 1, 2016 Jonus Enterprises declares a dividend of $5,000 to shareholders on record on July 4, 2016. Record the journal entry associated with this transaction. Jonus Enterprises uses the retained earnings method to record dividends.

Date	Account Title and Explanation	Debit	Credit

b) Record the journal entry when Jonus Enterprises pays out the dividend on August 15, 2016.

Date	Account Title and Explanation	Debit	Credit

Analysis

Both the cash dividend and retained earnings methods are acceptable accounting methods that produce the same result in recording cash dividend payouts. Why do you think some corporations prefer to use the cash dividends method, despite the fact it needs more entries than the other method? What advantages does that method offer to the corporation that chooses to use it?

AP-8A (⑤)

On November 1, 2016, Mistry Inc. declared $850,000 of dividends payable to shareholders on January 15, 2017. Outstanding are 220,000 common shares worth $2,000,000 and 30,000, $4 cumulative preferred shares worth $3,000,000. No new shares were issued during the year and dividends were last declared in 2012. Mistry had retained earnings of $4,500,000 at the beginning of 2016 and earned a net income of $1,200,000 during the year.

Required

a) Calculate how much Mistry Inc. owes the preferred shareholders.

---

b) Write the journal entry to record the declaration and subsequent payout of the dividends. Mistry uses the cash dividends method to record dividends.

Date	Account Title and Explanation	Debit	Credit

AP-9A (❻)

Bishop Lutz Hockey Paraphernalia Ltd. has 50,000 common shares issued. On January 1, 2016 the organization declared a 25% stock dividend. Prepare the journal entry to record the declaration and distribution (on February 1, 2016) of the dividend. The market price on the date of declaration was $15 per share. The company uses the stock dividends method to account for stock dividends.

Date	Account Title and Explanation	Debit	Credit

AP-10A (❺)

Martin Inc. was formed on January 1, 2014. Its shares were all issued during the first year of operations and were comprised as follows: 80,000 common shares and 10,000, $2 cumulative preferred shares. Over the past four years, Martin Inc. has declared and paid the following cash dividends.

Year	Total
2014	$30,000
2015	$35,000
2016	$0
2017	$45,000

Calculate the amount of dividends paid to each class of shareholders for each year.

Class of Shares	# of shares	2014	2015	2016	2017
Preferred Shares—cumulative	10,000				
Common Shares	80,000				
Total dividends paid		$30,000	$35,000	$0	$45,000

AP-11A (❸ ❺)

Given below is the equity section of Lizzy Dizzy Corporation at December 31, 2016. Preferred shares were sold at $100 each.

Lizzy Dizzy Corporation Shareholders' Equity As at December 31, 2016	
Share Capital	
Preferred Shares, $7, cumulative, 200,000 authorized	$20,000,000
Common Shares, unlimited authorized, 4,000,000 issued and outstanding	59,000,000
Total Share Capital	79,000,000
Retained Earnings	64,450,000
Total Shareholders' Equity	$143,450,000

Required

From the information provided above, calculate the following.

a) Calculate the number of preferred shares issued.

b) Calculate the total amount of annual dividend payable to preferred shareholders.

_____

_____

c) Calculate the average issuance price per common share.

_____

_____

d) Calculate the amount due to preferred shareholders if the company last declared dividends in 2012.

_____

_____

e) Suppose that the company declared to pay $25,000,000 as dividend on December 31, 2016 and paid dividends on January 10, 2017. Prepare journal entries to record the declaration and payment of dividends assuming the company uses the cash dividends method.

Date	Account Title and Explanation	Debit	Credit

AP-12A (❺)

On May 1, 2016, Crackle Canine Inc. declared $196,000 of dividends payable to shareholders on June 3, 2016. There are 24,800 common shares and 14,700, $1 cumulative preferred shares. Dividends were last paid in 2012. Write the journal entry to record the declaration and subsequent payout of the dividends. Assume the company uses the cash dividends method to record dividends.

Date	Account Title and Explanation	Debit	Credit

AP-13A (❺ ❾)

The shareholders' equity of Khan Corporation at January 1, 2016 was as follows.

Khan Corporation Shareholders' Equity As at January 1, 2016	
Share Capital	
Preferred Shares, $3, non-cumulative, 200,000 authorized, 2,000 issued and outstanding	$200,000
Common Shares, unlimited authorized, 32,000 issued and outstanding	1,200,000
Total Share Capital	1,400,000
Retained Earnings	320,000
Total Shareholders' Equity	$1,720,000

No dividend was declared for common shareholders. However on December 15, 2016 the directors decided to pay dividends to preferred shareholders. The dividend payment date was December 28, 2016. Net income for the year was $180,000. The company uses the retained earnings method to record dividends.

Required

a) Calculate the amount of dividend to be paid to preferred shareholders.

_____

_____

_____

_____

b) Prepare journal entry for declaration and payment of preferred dividend.

Date	Account Title and Explanation	Debit	Credit

c) Calculate the ending balance of retained earnings for the year ended December 31, 2016.

_____

_____

_____

_____

_____

_____

_____

_____

_____

_____

AP-14A (❻)

Tross Co. was incorporated and began operations on January 1, 2014. Tross Co. presented the following information at the end of the 2016 fiscal year.

Common Shares, unlimited authorized, 75,000 issued and outstanding	$225,000
Retained Earnings	148,000

Tross Co. declared a 15% stock dividend on December 31, 2016. The common shares were issued in 2014 for $3.00 each, but the current market price is $5.20 per share. The date of payment is January 5, 2017.

Prepare the journal entries to record the declaration and payment of the dividend. The company uses the retained earnings method to record dividends.

Date	Account Title and Explanation	Debit	Credit

AP-15A (❺ ❻)

Enigma Inc. is reaching the end of its fiscal year and has declared the following dividends.
- $20,000 cash dividend
- 10% stock dividend (on common shares)

The following information is also available.
- There are 10,000 common shares outstanding, issued for $12 per share
- There are 1,000, $5 non-cumulative preferred shares outstanding
- Common shares are currently trading for $10 per share
- For both dividends, the date of declaration is May 21, 2016 and the date of payment is May 31, 2016
- Enigma Inc. had net income of $45,000 during the year
- The balance of retained earnings at the beginning of the year was $123,500

Required

a) Prepare the journal entries to record the declaration and payment of the dividends. The company uses the cash dividend method to record dividends.

Date	Account Title and Explanation	Debit	Credit

b) Calculate the ending balance of retained earnings for the year.

_____

_____

_____

_____

_____

_____

_____

Analysis

Identify where each of the following accounts would be found on the balance sheet. The first one has been done as an example.

Cash	Current Assets
Common Shares	
Dividends Payable	
Retained Earnings	
Stock Dividends Distributable	

AP-16A (❺ ❾)

The shareholders' equity of Genghis Corporation at January 1, 2016 was as follows.

Genghis Corporation Shareholders' Equity As at January 1, 2016	
Share Capital	
Preferred Shares, $5, non-cumulative, 200,000 authorized, 1,000 issued and outstanding	$225,000
Common Shares, unlimited authorized, 35,000 issued and outstanding	1,070,000
Total Share Capital	1,295,000
Retained Earnings	253,000
Total Shareholders' Equity	$1,548,000

No dividend was declared for common shareholders. However on December 15, 2016 the directors decided to pay dividends to preferred shareholders. The dividend payment date was December 28, 2016. Net income for the year was $240,000. The company uses the cash dividends method to record dividends.

Required

a) Calculate the amount of dividend to be paid to preferred shareholders.

_____

_____

_____

b) Prepare the journal entry for the declaration and payment of the preferred dividend.

Date	Account Title and Explanation	Debit	Credit

c) Calculate the ending balance of retained earnings for the year ended December 31, 2016.

AP-17A (❸ ❹ ❺ ❾)

In 2016, Elizabeth and some of her friends invested money to start a company named FRIENDZ Corporation. The following transactions occurred during 2016.

Jan 1   The corporate charter authorized to issue 70,000, $5 cumulative preferred shares and unlimited common shares up to a maximum amount of $20,000,000.

Jan 6   Issued 200,000 common shares at $16 per share. Shares were issued to Elizabeth and other investors.

Jan 7   Issued another 500 common shares to Elizabeth in exchange for her services in organizing the corporation. The shareholders agreed that the services were worth $8,000.

Jan 12   Issued 3,500 preferred shares for $350,000.

Jan 14   Issued 10,000 common shares in exchange for a building acquired. For this purpose shares were valued at $16.

Nov 15   The first annual dividend on preferred shares was declared.

Dec 20   Paid the dividends declared on preferred shares.

FRIENDZ Corporation generated a $125,000 net income during the year. The company uses the retained earnings method to record dividends.

Required

a) Prepare the journal entries to record the above transactions in 2016.

Date	Account Title and Explanation	Debit	Credit

b) Calculate the ending balance of retained earnings for the year ended December 31, 2016.

_____

_____

_____

_____

_____

_____

_____

c) Prepare the shareholders' equity section of the balance sheet as at December 31, 2016.

AP-18A (❷ ❹ ❺ ❻)

In 2016, Joanna and some of her friends invested money to start a company named BUDZ Corporation. The following transactions occurred during 2016.

Jan 1   The corporate charter authorized 76,000, $4 cumulative preferred shares and unlimited common shares up to a maximum amount of $22,000,000 to be issued.

Jan 6   Issued 231,000 common shares at $15 per share. Shares were issued to Joanna and other investors.

Jan 7   Issued another 450 common shares to Joanna in exchange for her legal services in setting up the corporation. The shareholders agreed that the legal services were worth $6,750.

Jan 12   Issued 3,900 preferred shares for $321,000.

Jan 14   Issued 10,000 common shares in exchange for a building acquired. For this purpose shares were valued at $19.

Nov 15   The first annual dividend on preferred shares was declared.

Dec 20   Paid the dividends declared on preferred shares.

BUDZ Corporation generated a $147,000 net income during the year. Assume the company uses the retained earnings method to record dividends.

Required

a) Prepare the journal entries to record the above transactions.

Date	Account Title and Explanation	Debit	Credit

b) Calculate the ending balance of retained earnings for the year ended December 31, 2016.

_____

_____

_____

_____

_____

_____

c) Prepare the shareholders' equity section of the balance sheet as at December 31, 2016.

AP-19A (❸ ❺ ❻ ❽ ❾)

The shareholders' equity of East West Corporation at January 1, 2016 was as follows.

East West Corporation Shareholders' Equity As at January 1, 2016	
Share Capital	
Preferred Shares, $5, non-cumulative, 200,000 authorized, 1,000 issued and outstanding	$100,000
Common Shares, unlimited authorized, 30,000 issued and outstanding	1,500,000
Total Share Capital	1,600,000
Retained Earnings	1,970,000
Total Shareholders' Equity	$3,570,000

The following transactions occurred in 2016.

Jan 15   The Board decided to declare a total cash dividend of $120,000 to common and preferred shareholders.

Jan 28   Date of record of dividend.

Feb 10   Paid the cash dividend declared on January 15.

Nov 30   Declared a 20% stock dividend to common shareholders. Current market price was $55.

Dec 12   Distributed the stock dividends.

East West Corporation generated a $980,000 net income during the year. The company uses the cash and stock dividends method to record dividends.

Required

a) Prepare the journal entries to record the above transactions in 2016.

Date	Account Title and Explanation	Debit	Credit

b) Calculate the ending balance of retained earnings for the year ended December 31, 2016.

_____

_____

_____

_____

_____

_____

_____

_____

_____

c) Prepare the shareholders' equity section of the balance sheet as at December 31, 2016.

AP-20A (❶)

On March 31, 2016, Darred Inc. had 500,000 outstanding common shares. Its balance sheet on March 31, 2016 shows the common shares balance of $500,000 and the contributed surplus balance of zero. The following are the only changes to Darred's common shares that occurred between March 31, 2016 and March 31, 2017.

On April 1, 2016, Darred paid $10,000 cash to reacquire 15,000 of its own common shares.
On August 1, 2016, Darred reacquired an additional 30,000 shares for $60,000 cash.
On March 31, 2017, Darred issued 10,000 shares at $1.50 per share.

Required

a) Record the share reacquisition journal entry on April 1, 2016.

Date	Account Title and Explanation	Debit	Credit

b) Record the share reacquisition journal entry on August 1, 2016.

Date	Account Title and Explanation	Debit	Credit

c) After the share issuance on March 31, 2017, how many outstanding common shares would Darred have? Also, what would be Darred's common share balance and average cost of shares after the share issuance?

AP-21A (🕦)

The beginning balances of Adcha Corporation's shareholders' equity accounts for the fiscal year ending September 30, 2017 are as follows.

Common shares (unlimited number of shares authorized, 50,000 shares issued)	$150,000
Contributed surplus	7,000
Retained earnings	100,000

The following are the only transactions related to shareholders' equity that happened between September 30, 2016 and September 30, 2017.

On October 15, 2016, Adcha received $42,500 from issuing 5,000 common shares.
On May 30, 2017, Adcha paid $40,000 to repurchase 10,000 common shares.

Required

a) Record the share reacquisition journal entry on May 30, 2017.

Date	Account Title and Explanation	Debit	Credit

b) Fill in the number of shares issued (or outstanding) and the balances for all shareholders' equity accounts in the partial balance sheet on May 30, 2017 after the purchase of the shares.

Adcha Corporation	
Balance Sheet (partial)	
May 30, 2017	
Shareholders' equity	
Common shares (unlimited number of shares authorized, _____ shares issued)	
Contributed surplus	
Retained earnings	
Total shareholders' equity	

Application Questions Group B

AP-1B (❼)

At year-end on December 31, 2016, F'Brae Cheerleading Inc. has accounting income of $210,000. Write the journal entry to record the income tax expense. Assume the tax rate is 30%.

Date	Account Title and Explanation	Debit	Credit

AP-2B (❽)

Aniston Corporation has the following trial balance at the end of its fiscal year.

Aniston Corporation Trial Balance For the Year Ended December 31, 2016		
Account Title	**Debit**	**Credit**
Cash	$51,000	
Accounts Receivable	42,000	
Prepaid Insurance	5,000	
Accounts Payable		$36,000
Unearned Revenue		4,000
Common Shares		30,000
Retained Earnings		6,300
Sales Revenue		162,000
Cost of Goods Sold	72,900	
Insurance Expense	2,700	
Rent Expense	16,000	
Salaries and Wages Expense	38,000	
Depreciation Expense	2,300	
Income Tax Expense	8,400	
Totals	**$238,300**	**$238,300**

Complete the closing entries at year-end, using the income summary account.

Date	Account Title and Explanation	Debit	Credit

AP-3B (❽)

For the year 2016, Tinsmith Company experienced a net loss of $140,000. The revenues and expenses have already been closed to the income summary account. Prepare the final entry to complete the closing process, assuming that the company has a December 31 year-end.

Date	Account Title and Explanation	Debit	Credit

AP-4B (❸ ❾)

The shareholders' equity of Sharp Ltd. at December 31, 2016 is as follows.

Additional Information

- The preferred shares have an average issue price of $55 per share.
- The common shares have an average issue price of $40 per share.
- Retained earnings as at January 1, 2016 was $187,000, net income for the year was $65,450 and $9,800 of dividends were declared, payable on January 10, 2017

Fill in the grey areas in the table below with the correct numbers.

Sharp Ltd. Shareholders' Equity As at December 31, 2016	
Share Capital	
Preferred shares, $0.50, 5,000 shares authorized, 1,000 shares issued and outstanding	
Common shares, 30,000 shares authorized, 6,500 shares issued and outstanding	
Total Share Capital	
Retained Earnings	
Total Shareholders' Equity	

Analysis

Some corporations prefer to issue mainly preferred shares to their shareholders instead of common shares. Discuss reasons that might motivate a corporation to issue mainly preferred shares instead of common shares.

AP-5B (④)

Sherm & Co. issued 12,100 common shares for $91,000 on June 3, 2016.

Required

a) Write the journal entry to record the transaction.

Date	Account Title and Explanation	Debit	Credit

b) In addition to shares issued for cash, on June 3, 2016 Sherm & Co. issued an additional 13,600 common shares in exchange for machinery and a building. The machinery was valued at $61,000 and the building was valued at $101,000. The company could not readily determine the fair value of the shares. Record the transaction.

Date	Account Title and Explanation	Debit	Credit

c) The accountant that handled the issue of shares for Sherm & Co. has sent a bill for $5,600. The accountant has agreed to accept 550 common shares instead of cash. The company could not readily determine the fair value of the shares. Record the transaction on June 9, 2016.

Date	Account Title and Explanation	Debit	Credit

Analysis

In the case of non-monetary exchanges of assets and services exchanged for issued shares a corporation can choose to evaluate the fair value of shares issued with two options.

Option 1: Fair value of assets or services received

Option 2: Fair value of the shares issued

Think of a scenario when option 2 is preferred by accountants over option 1 and explain why.

_____

_____

_____

_____

_____

AP-6B (❹)

Flanders Inc. was formed on March 1, 2016. Upon formation, it issued 8,000 common shares for $22 each and 5,500 preferred shares for $30 each. In addition to the initial share issuance, the following share transaction occurred during the fiscal year.

Jun 7   Issued 1,000 common shares for $25 per share.

Aug 31   Issued 800 preferred shares for $33 per share.

Jan 9   Issued 2,500 common shares for $24 per share and 300 preferred shares for $32 per share.

Required

a) Prepare the journal entries to record the above transactions (including the entries to record the formation of Flanders Inc.).

Date	Account Title and Explanation	Debit	Credit

b) Determine the total number and value of common shares issued and outstanding as at March 31, 2017, by completing the following table.

Date	# of shares issued	$ per share	Total

Analysis

Suppose that Ned, the president of Flanders Inc., owns 990 of the outstanding preferred shares and 6,000 of the common shares. What percentage ownership does Ned have?

_____

_____

_____

_____

AP-7B (❺)

On February 1, 2016, Adam Enterprises declares a dividend of $4,800 to common shareholders to be paid on February 4.

Required

a) Record the journal entry associated with this transaction. Assume the company uses the cash dividends method to record dividends.

Date	Account Title and Explanation	Debit	Credit

b) Record the journal entry when Adam Enterprises pays out the dividend on February 4.

Date	Account Title and Explanation	Debit	Credit

Analysis

While a corporation is using the cash dividend method to record dividend payouts, cash dividend amounts are usually debited to the cash dividends account and credited to the dividends payable account on the date of declaration. When cash dividends are paid on the date of payment, the dividends payable account is debited. However, after the date of payment, there will still be debit balances in the cash dividends account. Record the journal entry that Adam Enterprises will have to make at year-end to close the cash dividends account.

Date	Account Title and Explanation	Debit	Credit

AP-8B (❺)

On December 1, 2016, Fickle Feline Inc. declared $200,000 of dividends payable to shareholders on January 3, 2017. There are 20,000 common shares worth $800,000 and 10,000, $0.50 cumulative preferred shares worth $500,000. No new shares were issued during the year and dividends were last declared in 2013. Fickle Feline had retained earnings of $2,500,000 at the beginning of 2016 and earned a net income of $650,000 during the year.

Required

a)   Calculate how much Fickle Feline Inc. owes the preferred shareholders.

b) Write the journal entry to record the declaration and subsequent payout of the dividends. Fickle Feline uses the cash dividends method to record dividends.

Date	Account Title and Explanation	Debit	Credit

AP-9B (❻)

Silang Vayman Ltd is a travel agency that specializes in tours to the Philippines and Russia. It has 75,000 common shares issued. On March 15, 2016, the organization declared a 45% stock dividend. Prepare the journal entry to record the declaration and distribution (on April 1, 2016) of the dividend. The market price on the date of declaration was $25 per share. The company uses the stock dividends method to account for stock dividends.

Date	Account Title and Explanation	Debit	Credit

AP-10B (❺)

Tilda Inc. was formed on January 1, 2015. Its shares were all issued during the first year of operations and were issued as follows: 10,000 common shares; 7,000, $4 cumulative preferred shares; and 4,000, $3 non-cumulative preferred shares. Over the past four years Tilda Inc. has declared and paid the following cash dividends.

Year	Total
2015	$60,000
2016	0
2017	100,000
2018	70,000

Calculate the amount of dividends paid to each class of shareholders for each year.

Class of Shares	# of shares	2015	2016	2016	2017
$4 Preferred—cumulative	7,000				
$3 Preferred—non-cumulative	4,000				
Common	10,000				
Total dividends paid		$60,000	$0	$100,000	$70,000

AP-11B (❸ ❺)

Given below is the equity section of Hudson Corporation at December 31, 2016.

Hudson Corporation **Shareholders' Equity** **As at December 31, 2016**	
Share Capital	
Preferred Shares, $12, non-cumulative, 100,000 authorized, 8,000 issued and outstanding	$800,000
Preferred Shares, $9, cumulative, 100,000 authorized, 20,000 issued and outstanding	2,000,000
Common Shares, unlimited authorized, 40,000 issued and outstanding	2,000,000
Total Share Capital	$4,800,000

Assume that no dividends were paid in 2014 or 2015. On December 31, 2016, Hudson Corporation declared a total cash dividend of $736,000.

Required

a) Calculate the amount of cash dividend paid to each of the three classes of share capital.

b) Calculate the dividend paid per share for each of the three classes of share capital.

_____

_____

_____

_____

c) Calculate the average issue price of each type of shares.

_____

_____

_____

_____

d) Prepare the journal entry for recording dividends in arrears for the last two years.

_____

_____

_____

AP-12B (❺)

Tea Time Inc. is a distributor of fine artisan tea and has a June 30 year-end. Due to several years of poor financial performance, dividends were last paid in 2013. On June 30, 2016 the company declared $100,000 of dividends. The dividends will be paid on July 5, 2016. As at June 30, 2016, the following shares were outstanding: 90,000 common shares; 40,000, $0.30 cumulative preferred shares; and 35,000, $0.20 non-cumulative preferred shares.

Required

a) Calculate how much Tea Time Inc. owes in dividends to each of the shareholders as at June 30, 2016.

_____

_____

_____

_____

b) Prepare the journal entry to record the declaration and subsequent payout of the dividends in 2016. Assume the company uses the cash dividend method to record dividends.

Date	Account Title and Explanation	Debit	Credit

AP-13B (❺ ❾)

On November 1, 2016, the financial records of Sam Inc. showed the following balances.

Sam Inc. Shareholders' Equity As at November 1, 2016	
Share Capital	
Preferred Shares, $5, cumulative, 200,000 authorized, 2,000 issued and outstanding	$200,000
Common Shares, unlimited authorized, 25,000 issued and outstanding	1,300,000
Total Share Capital	1,500,000
Retained Earnings	620,000
Total Shareholders' Equity	$2,120,000

On November 15, 2016, Sam Inc. declared $320,000 of dividends payable to shareholders. Dividends were last declared in 2013. The declared dividend was paid on December 5, 2016.

During the period November 1–December 31, 2016 the company earned a net income of $50,000.

Required

a) Calculate how much Sam Inc. owes the preferred shareholders.

_____

_____

_____

b) Prepare the journal entries to record the declaration and payment of dividends. The company uses the cash dividends method to record dividends.

Date	Account Title and Explanation	Debit	Credit

c) Calculate the ending balance of retained earnings for the two-month period of November 1–December 31, 2016.

_____

_____

_____

_____

_____

_____

AP-14B (❻)

On May 31, 2016, Red Synapse Corporation's shareholders' equity section shows the following balances.

Red Synapse Corporation Shareholders' Equity As at May 31, 2016	
Share Capital	
Common shares, unlimited authorized 30,000 shares issued and outstanding	$450,000
Retained Earnings	370,000
Total Shareholders' Equity	$820,000

Scenario 1

May 31   After preparing the shareholders' equity section shown above, the company declared and immediately distributed a 100% stock dividend. Current market price was $10. The company recorded the stock dividends by debiting retained earnings.

Required

a) Calculate the ending balance of retained earnings after the stock dividend.

_____

_____

_____

_____

_____

_____

b) Prepare the shareholders' equity section of balance sheet as at May 31, 2016 (after the stock dividend has been distributed).

Scenario 2

May 31   After preparing the shareholders' equity section shown at the beginning of this question, the company implemented a 2-for-1 stock split.

c) Calculate the number of outstanding shares.

_____

_____

_____

_____

d) Prepare the shareholders' equity section of the balance sheet as at May 31, 2016 (after the stock split).

AP-15B (❺ ❻)

At the end of Pataya Inc.'s third fiscal quarter in 2016, the shareholders' equity section of the balance sheet was as follows.

Pataya Inc. Shareholders' Equity As at September 30, 2016	
Share Capital	
Common Shares, unlimited authorized,	$960,000
60,000 issued and outstanding	
Retained Earnings	580,000
Total Shareholders' Equity	$1,540,000

In the fourth quarter of 2016, the following entries related to its equity accounts were recorded.

Date	Account Title and Explanation	Debit	Credit
Oct 2	Retained Earnings	110,000	
	Dividends Payable		110,000
Oct 25	Dividends Payable	110,000	
	Cash		110,000
Oct 31	Retained Earnings	140,000	
	Stock Dividends Distributable		140,000
Nov 5	Stock Dividends Distributable	140,000	
	Common Shares		140,000

Required

a) Explain each journal entry.

_____

_____

_____

_____

b) Complete the following table showing the equity balances at each indicated date.

	October 2	October 25	October 31	November 5
Common Shares				
Stock Dividends Distributable				
Retained Earnings				
Total Equity				

AP-16B (❹ ❻)

Vitamin Corporation was incorporated and began operations on May 1, 2012. Vitamin presented the following information at the end of the 2015 fiscal year.

Preferred Shares, $3 non-cumulative, 300,000 shares authorized, 5,000 shares issued and outstanding	$14,500
Common Shares, unlimited authorized, 40,000 shares issued and outstanding	280,000
Retained Earnings	645,000

Dividends were last paid out in 2014 fiscal year. The following transactions relating to shareholders' equity occurred during the 2016 to 2017 fiscal year.

May 1   Issued 60,000 common shares for $8 per share and 15,000 preferred shares for $3 per share.

Jun 2   Issued 5,000 common shares in exchange for $30,000 in legal services provided by Vitamin Corp.'s lawyer when setting up the corporation.

Aug 4   Issued 40,000 common shares in exchange for machinery valued at $250,000. The fair value of the shares could not be readily determined.

Nov 15 Issued 10,000 common shares for $8.50 each and 5,000 preferred shares for $3.25 each.

Apr 30 Net income for the year was $97,200. Dividends of $165,000 were declared and are payable on May 5, 2016. The company uses the cash dividends method to record dividends.

Required

a) Prepare the journal entries to record the above transactions.

Date	Account Title and Explanation	Debit	Credit

b) Calculate the ending balance of retained earnings for the 2016 fiscal year.

_____

_____

_____

_____

_____

_____

_____

_____

_____

_____

AP-17B (❸ ❹ ❺ ❾)

Gecko Inc. has the following in its shareholders' equity section of the balance sheet.

Gecko Inc. Shareholders' Equity As at December 31, 2015	
Share Capital	
Preferred shares, $0.50, 40,000 non-cumulative shares	$84,000
authorized, 12,000 shares issued and outstanding	
Common shares, 1,000,000 shares authorized,	337,500
75,000 shares issued and outstanding	
Total Share Capital	421,500
Retained Earnings	147,525
Total Shareholders' Equity	$569,025

The following transactions occurred during the year 2016.

Jan 9   Issued 20,000 common shares for $4.50 per share and 3,000 preferred shares for $7 per share.

Jun 7   Issued 4,000 preferred shares in exchange for equipment valued at $26,000 The fair value of the shares could not be readily determined.

Sep 8   Issued 12,000 common shares for $4.75 per share.

Oct 13   Declared $25,000 of dividends payable to shareholders on January 15, 2017. The company uses the cash dividends method to record dividends.

Dec 31   Net income for the year was $89,000.

Required

a) Prepare the journal entries to record the above transactions of 2016.

Date	Account Title and Explanation	Debit	Credit

b) Calculate the ending balance of retained earnings for the year 2016.

c) Prepare the shareholders' equity section of the balance sheet as at December 31, 2016.

AP-18B (❸ ❹ ❺ ❽ ❾)

Ping Pong Inc. began operations on January 1, 2015. The following transactions relating to shareholders' equity occurred in 2015, the first year of the company's operations.

Jan 1   The corporate charter authorized the issuance of unlimited common shares and 200,000, $3 non-cumulative preferred shares worth $100 each.

Jan 2   Issued 400,000 common shares for $11 per share.

Jan 3   Issued 200,000 common shares in exchange for a building valued at $730,000 and inventory valued at $320,000.

Jan 4   Instead of paying a $40,000 fee in cash, the company offered the accountant 400, $3 preferred shares.

Jan 5   Issued 15,000, $3 preferred shares for $100 cash per share.

For the year ended December 31, 2015, the newly incorporated company had a net income of $950,000. At the directors' meeting on January 15, 2016, the company decided to pay out 20% of net income as cash dividends to preferred and common shareholders. The date of record of the dividends is January 30, 2016. The company uses the cash dividend method to record cash dividends.

The dividend payment date is February 29, 2016. During the period January 1–February 29, 2016, the company had a net income of $160,000.

The following transaction was incurred by Ping Pong Inc. during the year ended December 31, 2016.

Jun 4   Issued 100,000 common shares for $15 per share.

For the year ended December 31, 2016, the company had a net income of $1,540,000. At the board of directors' meeting held on January 15, 2017, the company decided to pay out 25% of net income as cash dividends to preferred and common shareholders. The date of record of dividend is January 31, 2017.

The dividend is to be paid on February 28, 2017.

During the period January 1–February 28, 2017, the company had a net income of $250,000.

Required

a) Prepare journal entries to record the above transactions.

Date	Account Title and Explanation	Debit	Credit

Date	Account Title and Explanation	Debit	Credit

b) Calculate the ending balance of retained earnings for the year 2015.

_____

_____

_____

_____

_____

_____

c) Calculate the ending balance of retained earnings for the year 2016.

_____

_____

_____

_____

_____

_____

_____

d) Prepare the shareholders' equity section of the balance sheet as at December 31, 2015 and
    December 31, 2016.

AP-19B (❸ ❺ ❻ ❽ ❾)

At the beginning of 2016, Mystery Corporation had the following balances.

Share Capital	
Common shares, 1,000,000 shares authorized; 200,000 shares issued and outstanding	$2,000,000
Retained Earnings	925,000

The following transactions occurred during 2016.

Jan 10	The Board decided to declare $40,000 dividends to common shareholders.
Feb 15	Paid the cash dividend declared on January 10.
Nov 30	Declared a 20% stock dividend. The market value was $12 per share.
Dec 15	Distributed the stock dividend declared on November 30.

Mystery Corporation generated a $250,000 net income during the year. The company uses the retained earnings method to account for cash and stock dividends.

Required

a)   Prepare journal entries to record the above transactions.

Date	Account Title and Explanation	Debit	Credit

b)   Calculate the ending balance of retained earnings for the year ended December 31, 2016.

c) Prepare the shareholders' equity section of the balance sheet as at December 31, 2016.

AP-20B (❶)

On June 30, 2016, Choibok Corp. had 350,000 outstanding common shares. Its balance sheet on June 30, 2016 shows the common shares balance of $875,000 and the contributed surplus balance of zero. The following are the only changes to Choibok Corp.'s common shares that occurred after June 30, 2016.

On July 1, 2016, Choibok Corp. paid $30,000 cash to reacquire 15,000 of its own common shares.
On October 1, 2016, Choibok Corp. reacquired an additional 30,000 shares for $90,000 cash.
On December 1, 2016, Choibok Corp. issued 20,000 shares at $4 per share.

Required

a) Record the share reacquisition journal entry on July 1, 2016.

Date	Account Title and Explanation	Debit	Credit

b)   Record the share reacquisition journal entry on October 1, 2016.

Date	Account Title and Explanation	Debit	Credit

c)   After the share issuance on December 1, 2016, how many outstanding common shares would Choibok Corp. have? What will Choibok Corp.'s common share balance and average cost of shares be after the share issuance?

_____

_____

_____

_____

_____

_____

AP-21B (❶❶)

The beginning balances of Prakun Corporation's shareholders' equity accounts for the fiscal year ending December 31, 2016 are as follows.

Common shares (1,000,000 shares authorized, 70,000 shares issued)	$140,000
Contributed surplus	10,000
Retained earnings	180,000

The following are the only transactions related to shareholders' equity that happened between December 31, 2015 and December 31, 2016.

On February 15, 2016, Prakun received $110,000 from issuing 30,000 common shares.
On November 30, 2016, Prakun paid $40,000 to repurchase 10,000 common shares.

Required

a) Record the share reacquisition journal entry on November 30, 2016.

Date	Account Title and Explanation	Debit	Credit

b) Fill in the number of shares issued (or outstanding) and the balances for all shareholders'
    equity accounts in the partial balance sheet on November 30, 2016 after the purchase of
    the shares.

Prakun Corporation	
Balance Sheet (partial)	
November 30, 2016	
Shareholders' equity	
Common shares (1,000,000 shares authorized,	
_____ shares issued)	
Contributed surplus	
Retained earnings	
Total shareholders' equity	

Case Study

CS-1 ()

McIntosh Pharmaceutical develops and manufactures cancer-related drugs. For the last 10 years, it has been developing a unique chemical that has been shown to reduce the risk of breast cancer in middle-aged women. Unfortunately, just before going into mass production, scientists within McIntosh uncovered harmful side effects of the drug and strongly recommended to management that mass production be delayed for another five years to better study the drug. McIntosh management contemplated its response and after three days it announced this news to the public. Following the announcement, McIntosh's share price dropped 40%. During the three days of meetings, however, many managers decided to sell their shares in McIntosh.

Was their decision to sell shares ethically sound? Explain.

_____

_____

_____

_____

_____

_____

_____

_____

_____

_____

_____

_____

_____

_____

_____

_____

Critical Thinking

CT-1 (❻)

John Maynard Nash, a budding economist, noticed that the market price of shares seemed to decline after the date of record of a cash dividend. Can you suggest why this might be the case?

_____

_____

_____

_____

_____

_____

_____

_____

_____

_____

_____

_____

_____

_____

_____

_____

_____

_____

Notes

Chapter 7

CORPORATIONS: THE FINANCIAL STATEMENTS

LEARNING OUTCOMES

❶ Explain the different requirements for public and private companies when presenting financial statements

❷ Prepare an income statement and a statement of comprehensive income

❸ Prepare a statement of retained earnings and a statement of changes in equity

❹ Record and report on prior period adjustments

❺ Prepare a balance sheet and a statement of financial position

❻ Calculate and explain earnings per share

❼ Calculate ratios used to evaluate earnings and dividend performance

AMEENGAGE™ *Access **ameengage.com** for integrated resources including tutorials, practice exercises, the digital textbook and more.*

—————— Assessment Questions ——————

AS-1 (❶)

Describe the differences between users of corporate financial statements and users of proprietorship financial statements.

_____

_____

_____

_____

_____

_____

_____

_____

_____

_____

AS-2 (❶)

Is a partnership, which is a private company, allowed to adopt IFRS in Canada?

_____

_____

AS-3 (❶)

Is a public corporation allowed to adopt ASPE in Canada?

_____

_____

AS-4 (❷)

Define a business segment. How does a business segment relate to discontinued operations?

_____

_____

_____

_____

_____

AS-5 (❷)

Define discontinued operations and briefly discuss the reporting requirements for discontinued operations under ASPE and IFRS.

_____

_____

_____

_____

_____

_____

AS-6 (❷)

Define other comprehensive income.

_____

_____

_____

AS-7 (❷)

How should other comprehensive income (OCI) be reported under IFRS? Provide specific examples of OCI.

_____

_____

_____

_____

_____

AS-8 (❷)

IFRS requires that expenses on the statement of comprehensive income be presented either by function or by nature. Briefly describe each of the two methods.

_____

_____

_____

_____

_____

_____

_____

_____

AS-9 (❸)

True or False: When a public company sells additional common shares to the public, it must always report the changes in the value of common shares on its statement of changes in equity. Explain.

_____

_____

_____

_____

AS-10 (❸)

Briefly discuss the major differences between the statement of retained earnings under ASPE and the statement of changes in equity under IFRS.

_____

_____

_____

_____

_____

_____

_____

AS-11 (❹)

List the three types of accounting changes that warrant a prior period adjustment.

_____

_____

_____

_____

AS-12 (❹)

What is the accounting treatment for correcting prior period errors?

_____

_____

_____

_____

_____

_____

_____

_____

_____

AS-13 (❺)

How are assets typically listed on the statement of financial position under IFRS?

_____

_____

_____

_____

_____

_____

_____

_____

_____

AS-14 (◐)

Name a key profitability indicator that is required to be presented on the statement of comprehensive income by a public company under IFRS and provide the formula to arrive at this indicator.

_____

_____

_____

_____

_____

_____

_____

_____

_____

_____

AS-15 (◐)

Why is the weighted average number of shares outstanding used as a denominator when calculating earnings per share? How is the weighted average number of shares calculated?

_____

_____

_____

_____

_____

_____

_____

_____

AS-16 (6)

Briefly describe the difference between a basic earnings per share calculation and a fully diluted earnings per share calculation.

_____

_____

_____

_____

_____

_____

_____

_____

_____

_____

_____

_____

_____

_____

_____

_____

_____

_____

_____

_____

_____

_____

_____

AS-17 (❼)

Explain what the book value per common share ratio indicates and provide a formula to calculate this ratio.

_____

_____

_____

_____

_____

_____

_____

_____

_____

_____

_____

_____

_____

_____

_____

_____

_____

_____

_____

_____

_____

AS-18 (❼)

Why would investors be interested to know the dividend payout ratio of a given corporation and how would they arrive at this figure?

_____

_____

_____

_____

_____

_____

_____

_____

_____

_____

AS-19 (❼)

What does a high price-earnings ratio usually indicate?

_____

_____

_____

_____

_____

_____

_____

_____

AS-20 (❷)

Name at least three items that are often included in the other income or expenses section of the income statement under ASPE.

_____

_____

_____

_____

_____

AS-21 (❷)

Provide at least two examples of items that are usually included in the discontinued operations section of the income statement under ASPE.

_____

_____

_____

AS-22 (❷ ❸)

Explain the difference between other comprehensive income and accumulated other comprehensive income on financial statements.

_____

_____

_____

_____

_____

_____

_____

_____

Application Questions Group A

AP-1A (❷)

Green Light Emissions Everyday (otherwise known as GLEE Corporation) has sales of $400,000 and Cost of Goods Sold of $120,000 for the year ended December 31, 2016. It also has salaries expense of $80,000 and miscellaneous operating expenses of $20,000. Prepare an income statement under ASPE taking into account income tax expense. Assume a tax rate of 30%.

AP-2A (❷)

Budokan Company, a corporation with a December 31 year-end, has sales of $530,000, cost of goods sold of $120,000, selling expense of $70,000, administrative expense of $200,000, tax expense of $40,000 and basic and diluted earnings per share of $5.5 in 2016.

Required

a) Prepare an income statement under ASPE for the year ended December 31, 2016.

b) Prepare a statement of comprehensive income (by function) under IFRS for the year ended December 31, 2016.

AP-3A (❷)

Born off the coast of Mykonos, Gregory displayed an aptitude for singing at a very early age. In high school, he joined a musical club that participated in numerous singing competitions. Gregory wants to start his own singing school and is taking an accounting course to help him become financially literate. He is posed with the following question on his test. Help him solve this question.

"Nacho Libray Inc. follows ASPE and has income from operations of $200,000. Their total other expenses amounted to $100,000 and the income tax expense was $40,000. Calculate the net income for the year."

AP-4A (❸)

The following information was taken from the accounting records of Montana Inc. at May 31, 2016. Montana Inc. is a private corporation and follows ASPE.

Assume a tax rate of 37%. During the year, no shares were issued or redeemed.

Line Item	Amount
Total dividends paid	$61,000
Retained earnings, June 1, 2015	110,000
Net Income	156,000

Prepare a statement of retained earnings for Montana Inc. for the year ended May 31, 2016.

AP-5A (❸)

Top Cuisine Inc. has a March 31 year-end. Retained earnings at March 31, 2015 had a credit balance of $54,700. During the 2016 fiscal year, net income was $24,615 and dividends of $12,600 were declared and paid. During the 2017 fiscal year, Top Cuisine had a net loss of $16,680 and dividends of $10,400 were declared but not yet paid.

Prepare statements of retained earnings for Top Cuisine Inc. as at March 31, 2016 and March 31, 2017.

AP-6A (❹)

On March 17, 2016, the bookkeeper for GIFT Inc. noticed that she made an error when recording a $44,000 expenditure in the prior fiscal year. She booked the amount to the Repairs and Maintenance expense account instead of posting to the Equipment account. Write the journal entry that should be recorded to correct the Equipment account. Ignore the impact of depreciation. Assume the tax rate is 30%.

Date	Account Title and Explanation	Debit	Credit

AP-7A (❹)

On April 4, 2016, an auditor noticed that TFK Inc. accidently recorded an insurance expenditure of $50,000 as an expense instead of as a prepaid. The purchase was made on the last day of the fiscal period. Write the journal entry that should be recorded in the next fiscal period to correct the Prepaid Insurance account. Assume the tax rate is 30%.

Date	Account Title and Explanation	Debit	Credit

AP-8A (❷ ❸)

Below is the adjusted trial balance for Simple Town Corporation. The balance of retained earnings represents the balance at the beginning of the fiscal year. The company decided not to pay dividends this year.

Simple Town Corporation Adjusted Trial Balance June 30, 2016	Debit	Credit
Cash	$78,000	
Accounts Receivable	93,000	
Prepaid Rent	7,800	
Inventory	195,000	
Notes Receivable	35,000	
Furniture	120,000	
Accumulated Depreciation		$42,000
Accounts Payable		24,000
Unearned Revenue		22,500
Interest Payable		6,800
Salaries Payable		18,000
Loan Payable		80,000
Preferred Shares		25,800
Common Shares		105,000
Retained Earnings (beginning balance)		171,290
Sales Revenue		300,000
Net Change in Fair Value of Investments		2,800
Sales Returns and Allowances	12,000	
Cost of Goods Sold	60,000	
Depreciation Expense	12,600	
Salaries Expense	69,000	
Rent Expense	16,500	
Utilities Expense	19,500	
Insurance Expense	23,400	
Supplies Expense	36,000	
Income Tax Expense	17,990	
Loss on Disposal of Equipment	2,400	
Total	$798,190	$798,190

Required

a) Prepare an income statement for the year ended June 30, 2016.

b) Prepare the statement of retained earnings for Simple Town Corporation.

c) If the company followed IFRS, what amount would be shown under other comprehensive income on the statement? Assume the tax rate was 40%.

AP-9A (❷)

Spader Inc. had the following account balances at the end of the year. Prepare a multistep income statement for December 31, 2016. Spader Inc. follows ASPE.

Account Title	Balance
Cost of Goods Sold	$234,000
Depreciation Expense	6,200
Loss on Sale of Assets from Discontinued Operations	5,700
Insurance Expense	2,700
Loss on Foreign Currency Translation	600
Income Tax Expense (Continuing Operations)	27,780
Income Tax Expense (Discontinued Operations)	2,220
Maintenance Expense	3,800
Operating Income from Discontinued Operations	16,800
Rent Expense	32,000
Salaries Expense	87,500
Sales Returns and Allowances	3,900
Sales Revenue	520,000
Telephone Expense	4,100
Travel Expense	6,300

Required

a) Prepare a multistep income statement for December 31, 2016.

b) If the company had followed IFRS, where would the loss on foreign currency translation go on the statement of comprehensive income?

_____

_____

AP-10A (⑤)

Below is the adjusted trial balance for Home Care Solutions Inc.

Home Care Solutions Inc. Adjusted Trial Balance June 30, 2016	Debit	Credit
Accounts Payable		$71,200
Accounts Receivable	$80,000	
Accumulated Depreciation		28,000
Cash	63,850	
Common Shares		10,400
Cost of Goods Sold	96,000	
Depreciation Expense	35,200	
Insurance Expense	36,000	
Interest Expense	21,120	
Interest Payable		14,960
Inventory	90,000	
Loan Payable		176,000
Preferred Shares		7,200
Prepaid Rent	28,000	
Equipment	176,000	
Rent Expense	66,000	
Retained Earnings (after Dividends)		40,810
Salary Expense	72,000	
Salary Payable		34,000
Sales Returns	12,000	
Sales Revenue		400,000
Unearned Revenue		49,600
Utilities Expense	56,000	
Total	$832,170	$832,170

Additional Information
- Net income for the year was $5,680 and the retained earnings at July 1, 2015 was $44,960. Dividends of $4,150 were declared and paid in the year.
- Home Care Solutions has a loan payable due in 8 years. The principal payments are $2,800 per month.
- 1,440 $2, cumulative preferred shares have been issued and 15,000 have been authorized. 3,000 common shares have been issued and 45,000 have been authorized.

Required

a) Prepare a classified balance sheet as at June 30, 2016 under ASPE.

b) Where does the accumulated other comprehensive income account appear on this company's balance sheet? Explain.

_____

_____

_____

AP-11A (❺)

Sigmund Corporation has the following account balances. Using this information, prepare a classified balance sheet as at December 31, 2016 under ASPE.

Account Title	Balance
Accounts Payable	$56,000
Accounts Receivable	47,500
Accumulated Depreciation	8,600
Bank Loan	110,000
Cash	17,000
Common Shares	42,000
Inventory	65,500
Preferred Shares	50,000
Prepaid Rent	12,000
Machinery	220,000
Retained Earnings	91,900
Unearned Revenue	3,500

Notes

Unlimited common shares are authorized and 2,000 have been issued.

5,000 preferred shares are authorized and 500 have been issued.

The bank loan is payable over four years and $27,500 will be paid by December 31, 2017.

AP-12A (❼)

Part of the financial statements of Toromont Industries is shown below.

Statement of Retained Earnings For the Year Ended December 31, 2016 ($ thousands)	
Retained Earnings, January 1, 2016	$477,820
Add: Net Income for the Period	122,280
	570,100
Less: Cash Dividends	(31,061)
Retained Earnings, December 31, 2016	$539,039

Calculate the Dividend Payout Ratio and discuss.

_____

_____

_____

_____

_____

AP-13A (❼)

The following data is available for two companies, Sam Corporation and Tally Corporation for the year ended December 31, 2016. Both corporations do not have any preferred shares.

	Sam Corporation	Tally Corporation
Income from continuing operations (net of tax)	$710,000	$510,000
Income from discontinued operations (net of tax)	120,000	60,000
Net income	830,000	570,000
Shares outstanding during the year: 100,000 shares by Sam and 50,000 shares by Tally	800,000	450,000
Beginning retained earnings	2,070,000	1,580,000
Current liabilities	560,000	420,000
Non-current liabilities	980,000	760,000
Market price per share	14	11
Total dividends paid	200,000	120,000

Required

a) Calculate the following ratios for both companies.

1. EPS Ratio
2. Dividend Payout Ratio
3. Price-Earnings Ratio

1. EPS Ratio

	Sam Corporation	Tally Corporation
EPS Ratio		

2. Dividend Payout Ratio

	Sam Corporation	Tally Corporation
Dividend Payout Ratio		

3. Price-Earnings Ratio

	Sam Corporation	Tally Corporation
Price-Earnings Ratio		

b) Compare the performance and position of the two companies by interpreting the ratios calculated in part a).

_____

_____

_____

_____

_____

_____

_____

_____

AP-14A (❷ ❸ ❺)

Below is a list of accounts and balances for FlipFlop Inc. for the year ending June 30, 2016. Based on the information provided, answer the required questions. FlipFlop Inc. follows ASPE.

Account Title	Balance
Accounts Payable	$8,900
Accounts Receivable	6,100
Accumulated Depreciation	1,200
Bank Loan	21,000
Cash	19,000
Cash Dividends	3,500
Common Shares	10,000
Cost of Goods Sold	13,500
Depreciation Expense	700
Gain on Sale of Assets from Discontinued Operations	2,000
Insurance Expense	600
Interest Expense	120
Interest Revenue	280
Income Tax Expense (Continuing Operations)	1,516
Income Tax Expense (Discontinued Operations)	2,000
Inventory	18,000
Maintenance Expense	590
Operating Income from Discontinued Operations	8,000
Prepaid Insurance	3,250
Professional Fees Expense	260
Equipment	25,000
Rent Expense	1,000
Retained Earnings (beginning balance)	17,986
Salaries Expense	2,500
Sales Discounts	1,100
Sales Returns and Allowances	840
Sales Revenue	30,000
Telephone Expense	90
Travel Expense	1,400
Unearned Revenue	1,700

Notes

Unlimited common shares are authorized and 2,000 have been issued.
The bank loan is payable over five years and $4,200 will be paid by June 30, 2017.

Required

a)   Prepare a multistep income statement for the year ending June 30, 2016.

b) Prepare a statement of retained earnings for the year ended June 30, 2016.

c) Prepare a classified balance sheet as at June 30, 2016.

d) If the company had followed IFRS, how would the section of assets on the statement of financial position be different?

_____

_____

_____

AP-15A (❷ ❸ ❺)

Below is the adjusted trial balance for SandStone Corp. as at September 30, 2016.

SandStone Corp. Adjusted Trial Balance September 30, 2016	Debit	Credit
Accounts Payable		$20,470
Accounts Receivable	$23,000	
Accumulated Depreciation		8,050
Cash	19,550	
Common Shares		8,750
Cost of Goods Sold	40,250	
Depreciation Expense	10,120	
Gain on Disposal of Equipment		2,530
Gain on Sale of Assets from Discontinued Operations		13,400
Income Tax Benefit (Continuing Operations)		10,788
Income Tax Benefit (Discontinued Operations)		6,240
Insurance Expense	10,350	
Interest Expense	5,520	
Interest Payable		3,910
Inventory	25,875	
Loan Payable		46,000
Loss from Discontinued Operations	29,000	
Preferred Shares		5,890
Prepaid Insurance	8,050	
Equipment	50,600	
Rent Expense	19,550	
Retained Earnings		35,512
Sales Discounts	11,060	
Salary Expense	20,700	
Salary Payable		9,775
Sales Returns and Allowances	3,450	
Sales Revenue		115,000
Supplies Expense	7,400	
Unearned Revenue		14,260
Utilities Expense	16,100	
Total	$300,575	$300,575

Required

a) Prepare a multi-step income statement for the year ended September 30, 2016 under ASPE.

b) The balance of retained earnings in the adjusted trial balance represents the beginning balance at October 1, 2015. No dividends were declared during the year. Prepare a statement of retained earnings for the year ended September 30, 2016.

c) Prepare a classified balance sheet as at September 30, 2016. Additional information is as follows.

- The loan payable is due over four years. The principal payments are $1,050 each month.
- Preferred shares: $1, cumulative, 55,000 authorized, 7,800 issued and outstanding
- Common shares: 100,000 authorized, 15,900 issued and outstanding

Application Questions Group B

AP-1B (❷)

Black Light Environment Everyday (otherwise known as BLEE Inc.) has sales of $370,000 and cost of goods sold of $100,000 for the year ended June 30, 2016. It also has salaries expense of $75,000 and miscellaneous operating expenses of $21,000. Prepare a basic income statement on June 30, 2016 for BLEE, taking into account income tax expense. Assume a tax rate of 31%.

AP-2B (❷)

Venus Space Explorations, a corporation with a June 30, 2016 year end, has sales of $420,000, cost of goods sold of $200,000, salaries expense of $40,000, rent expense of $24,000 , supplies expense of $10,000, tax expense of $42,000, and basic and diluted earnings per share of $1.50.

Required

a) Prepare an income statement under ASPE for Venus for the year ended June 30, 2016.

b) Prepare a statement of comprehensive income (by nature) under IFRS for Venus for the year ended June 30, 2016.

AP-3B (❷)

Gleek the Geek Corporation follows IFRS. In 2016, it has income from continuing operations of $700,000, income from discontinued operations (net of income tax expense) of $50,000, and other comprehensive income (net of income tax) of $13,000.

Required

a) Calculate Gleek the Geek's net income for 2016.

b) Calculate Gleek the Geek's total comprehensive income for 2016.

AP-4B (❸)

Below is the adjusted trial balance for Connection Communications Inc. for the month of September 2016. Dividends of $5,800 were declared and paid in the month.

Connection Communications Inc. Adjusted Trial Balance September 30, 2016		
	Debit	**Credit**
Accounts Payable		$5,176
Accounts Receivable	$20,057	
Accumulated Depreciation		11,325
Cash	16,822	
Common Shares		11,600
Cost of Goods Sold	12,940	
Depreciation Expense	3,395	
Insurance Expense	1,545	
Interest Expense	1,225	
Interest Payable		2,083
Loan Payable		24,500
Preferred Shares		4,500
Prepaid Insurance	1,850	
Property, Plant and Equipment	32,350	
Rent Expense	3,550	
Retained Earnings (after dividends)		23,300
Salary Expense	8,160	
Salary Payable		3,882
Sales Revenue		64,700
Supplies	42,055	
Supplies Expense	7,764	
Unearned Revenue		4,852
Utilities Expense	4,205	
Total	$155,918	$155,918

Prepare a statement of retained earnings for the month ended September 30, 2016.

AP-5B (❸ ❹)

Kensington Corporation has a December 31 year-end. Retained earnings as at December 31, 2014 had a debit balance of $15,450. During the 2015 fiscal year net income was $91,550 and dividends of $34,500 were declared and paid. During the 2016 fiscal year Kensington had a net income of $32,100 and dividends of $28,000 were declared and paid. An audit revealed that the 2015 net income was understated by a net value of $5,200. A new engine was recorded as an expense when it should have been recorded as an asset.

Required

a) Complete Kensington Corporation's statement of retained earnings for 2015.

b) Complete Kensington Corporation's statement of retained earnings for 2016.

AP-6B (❹)

On January 31, 2016, the bookkeeper for FLAX Inc. noticed that she made an error when recording a $96,000 expenditure in the prior fiscal year. She booked the amount to the Repairs and Maintenance expense account instead of posting to the Equipment account. Write the journal entry that should be recorded to correct the Equipment account. Ignore the impact of depreciation. Assume the tax rate is 30%.

Date	Account Title and Explanation	Debit	Credit

Analysis

What if the error were reversed? Write the journal entry that would have to be made if the $96,000 expense were incorrectly recorded as equipment.

Date	Account Title and Explanation	Debit	Credit

AP-7B (❹)

On January 31, 2016, an auditor noticed that MDK Inc. accidently recorded an insurance expenditure of $60,000 as an expense instead of as a prepaid. The purchase was made on the last day of the fiscal period. Write the journal entry that should be recorded in the next fiscal period to correct the Prepaid Insurance account. Assume the tax rate is 30%.

Date	Account Title and Explanation	Debit	Credit

Analysis

Both ASPE and IFRS require the retrospective approach for both correction of prior period errors and accounting policy changes. However, the prospective approach is required for a change in accounting estimate. Why do you think the prospective approach is required for a change in accounting estimate?

_____

_____

_____

_____

_____

_____

AP-8B (❷ ❸)

Below is the adjusted trial balance for Del Ray Company. Dividends paid during the year were $7,800.

Del Ray Company Adjusted Trial Balance March 31, 2016		
	Debit	Credit
Cash	$33,800	
Accounts Receivable	40,300	
Prepaid Insurance	5,070	
Supplies	84,500	
Property, Plant and Equipment	65,000	
Accumulated Depreciation		$22,750
Accounts Payable		10,400
Unearned Revenue		9,750
Interest Payable		2,250
Loan Payable		25,000
Preferred Shares		14,500
Common Shares		21,700
Retained Earnings (after dividends)		116,110
Sales Revenue		130,000
Gain on Disposal of Equipment		5,200
Sales Discounts	650	
Sales Returns and Allowances	1,950	
Cost of Goods Sold	26,000	
Depreciation Expense	7,150	
Salary Expense	29,900	
Rent Expense	7,150	
Utilities Expense	8,450	
Insurance Expense	10,400	
Supplies Expense	15,600	
Interest Expense	1,250	
Income Tax Expense (Continuing Operations)	8,010	
Income Tax Expense (Discontinued Operations)	2,880	
Income from Discontinued Operations	8,100	
Gain on Sale of Assets from Discontinued Operations	1,500	
Total	$357,660	$357,660

Required

a) Prepare an income statement for the year ended March 31, 2016 under ASPE.

b) Prepare the statement of retained earnings for Del Ray.

c) If the company adhered to IFRS , there was no specific rule on how to present the expenses on the statement of comprehensive income. Is that true or false? Explain.

_____

_____

_____

_____

_____

AP-9B (❷ ❸)

The following information was taken from the accounting records of Splinter Inc. at December 31, 2016. Splinter Inc. is a public corporation and follows IFRS.

Line Item	Amount
Common shares, 50,000 outstanding on January 1, 2016	$350,000
Common shares, 70,000 outstanding on December 31, 2016	120,000
Cost of Goods Sold	468,000
Dividends paid	50,000
Gain on Sale of Assets	6,200
General operating expenses	210,000
Income tax expense on continuing operations	29,850
Income tax expense on operating income from discontinued operations	18,600
Interest Expense	8,700
Operating income from discontinued operations	62,000
Prior year error—debit to Retained Earnings	6,000
Retained Earnings, January 1, 2016 (prior to adjustment)	410,000
Sales revenue	780,000

Required

a) Prepare the statement of comprehensive income for the year ended December 31, 2016.

b) Prepare the statement of changes in equity for the year ended December 31, 2016 showing the changes in contributed capital and retained earnings.

AP-10B (⑤)

Below is the adjusted trial balance for Busy Town Inc.

Busy Town Inc. Adjusted Trial Balance December 31, 2016		
	Debit	**Credit**
Accounts Payable		$69,420
Accounts Receivable	$78,000	
Accumulated Depreciation		27,300
Cash	66,300	
Common Shares		147,500
Cost of Goods Sold	93,600	
Depreciation Expense	34,320	
Insurance Expense	35,100	
Interest Payable		936
Interest Receivable	1,560	
Interest Revenue		10,400
Inventory	87,750	
Non-Current Debt		46,800
Loss on Sale of Equipment	1,800	
Notes Receivable	130,000	
Preferred Shares		148,530
Short-Term Investment	27,300	
Equipment	171,600	
Rent Expense	64,350	
Retained Earnings		5,784
Salary Expense	70,200	
Salary Payable		33,150
Sales Returns	11,700	
Sales Revenue		390,000
Unearned Revenue		48,360
Utilities Expense	54,600	
Total	$928,180	$928,180

Additional Information
- Net income for the year was $34,730 and retained earnings at January 1, 2016 was $70,484. Dividends of $64,700 were declared and paid in the year.
- Busy Town has a note receivable that matures in December 2019, with no installment payments received until maturity. Busy Town also has long term debt that is due in 4 years. The principal payments are $975 per month.
- Preferred shares are $1, non-cumulative; 95,000 shares have been authorized and 24,700 shares are issued and outstanding. For common shares, 200,000 shares have been authorized and 29,800 shares have been issued.

Prepare a classified balance sheet as at December 31, 2016 under ASPE.

AP-11B (❷ ❸ ❺)

Below is the adjusted trial balance for Excel Network Inc. as at December 31, 2016.

Excel Network Inc.		
Adjusted Trial Balance		
December 31, 2016		
	Debit	Credit
Cash	$84,000	
Accounts Receivable	189,000	
Prepaid Rent	9,240	
Inventory	210,000	
Equipment	43,000	
Accumulated Depreciation		$15,050
Accounts Payable		38,000
Unearned Revenue		35,625
Interest Payable		8,925
Salary Payable		28,500
Loan Payable		105,000
Preferred Shares		75,000
Common Shares		105,000
Retained Earnings (after dividends)		111,805
Sales Revenue		475,000
Sales Returns	19,000	
Cost of Goods Sold	166,250	
Depreciation Expense	4,515	
Salary Expense	109,250	
Rent Expense	26,125	
Interest Expense	12,600	
Utilities Expense	30,875	
Insurance Expense	37,050	
Supplies Expense	57,000	
Total	$997,905	$997,905

Required

a) Prepare a multi-step income statement for the year ended December 31, 2016 under ASPE. Ignore income taxes.

b) The retained earnings at January 1, 2016 were $160,305 and dividends of $48,500 were declared in the year. Prepare a statement of retained earnings for the year ended December 31, 2016.

c) Prepare a classified balance sheet as at December 31, 2016. Additional information as of December 31, 2016 is as follows.

- The loan payable is due over five years. The principal payments are $1,000 for each month.
- Preferred shares: $8, cumulative, 100,000 shares authorized, 25,000 have been issued and are outstanding
- Common shares: unlimited number of shares authorized, 46,000 shares have been issued and are outstanding

AP-12B (7)

Shown below is a section of the statement of financial position of You Co.

Shareholders' Equity	
Common Shares, unlimited shares authorized, 562,652 shares issued and outstanding	$2,169,856
Retained Earnings	1,733,427
Accumulated Other Comprehensive Income	30,283
Total Shareholders' Equity	3,933,566
Total Liabilities and Shareholders' Equity	$5,511,187

Required

a) Calculate the book value per share for 2016.

Shareholders' Equity	
Shares—End of Year	
Book Value per Share	

b) Calculate the basic earnings per share for You Co. based on the following income statement.

Net income	$1,293,897
Earnings per share	
Basic	?
Diluted	$2.26

Analysis

In this chapter, you have learned how to calculate earnings per share. Often, a corporation's annual report will report earnings per share as calculated by the corporation. Rarely do the corporation's reported earnings per share agree with a financial analyst's calculation of this number. Discuss why these two calculations may differ.

_____

_____

_____

_____

_____

_____

_____

_____

AP-13B (❻)

Marry Inc. provided the following information from its accounting records for the years ending December 31, 2017 and 2016.

	2017	2016
Income from continuing operations (net of tax)	$840,000	$740,000
Income from discontinued operations (net of tax)	150,000	70,000
Net Income	990,000	810,000
Each year, 100,000 common shares were outstanding	1,000,000	1,000,000
Beginning retained earnings	1,990,000	1,580,000
Current liabilities	560,000	420,000
Non-current debt	980,000	760,000
Market price per share	15	13
Total dividends paid	500,000	400,000

No shares were issued or redeemed during the two years. The company has never issued any preferred shares.

Required

Calculate the following ratios for both years.

a) EPS Ratio

	2017	2016
EPS Ratio		

b) Income per Share

	2017	2016
Income from Continuing Operations per Share		
Income from Discontinued Operations per Share		
Net Income per Share		

c) Dividend Payout Ratio

	2017	2016
Dividend Payout Ratio		

d) Price – Earnings Ratio

	2017	2016
Price – Earnings Ratio		

e) Book Value per Share

	2017	2016
Book Value per Share		

Analysis

Price-earnings ratio (or P/E ratio) is generally regarded by many investors as a reliable indicator of a stock's potential growth in the future. One of your clients just told you that a stock he invested just had a significant growth in the P/E ratio, yet the price of that share has not changed. How would you explain to him about why P/E ratio increases without an increase in the share price?

_____

_____

_____

_____

_____

_____

AP-14B (❷ ❸ ❺)

Below is the adjusted trial balance for Elements Inc. as at March 31, 2016.

Elements Inc. Adjusted Trial Balance March 31, 2016		
	Debit	**Credit**
Accounts Payable		$19,580
Accounts Receivable	$22,000	
Accumulated Depreciation		7,700
Cash	18,700	
Common Shares		21,500
Cost of Goods Sold	37,400	
Depreciation Expense	9,900	
Insurance Expense	9,900	
Interest Payable		660
Interest Receivable	1,320	
Interest Revenue		2,640
Inventory	24,750	
Non-Current Debt		13,200
Loss on Disposal of Machinery	1,485	
Notes Receivable	33,000	
Preferred Shares		19,850
Prepaid Insurance	7,700	
Furniture	49,500	
Rent Expense	18,150	
Retained Earnings (after dividends)		54,185
Salary Expense	19,800	
Salary Payable		9,350
Sales Returns and Allowances	3,300	
Sales Revenue		110,000
Unearned Revenue		13,640
Utilities Expense	15,400	
Total	$272,305	$272,305

a) Prepare a multi-step income statement for the year ended March 31, 2016 under ASPE. Ignore taxes for this question.

b) Retained earnings at April 1, 2015 had a credit balance of $68,335 and dividends of $14,150 were declared and paid in the year. Prepare a statement of retained earnings for the year ended March 31, 2016.

c) Prepare a classified balance sheet as at March 31, 2016. Additional information as of March 31, 2016 is as follows.

- The long term debt is due over four years. The principal payments are $275 each month.
- Preferred shares: $0.50, non-cumulative, 15,000 shares authorized, 13,233 shares issued and outstanding
- Common shares: 21,000 shares authorized, 19,550 shares issued and outstanding
- The note receivable will not be paid until December 2017.

d) If the company had followed IFRS, would the statement of retained earnings be the same as part b)? Explain.

_____

_____

_____

AP-15B (❷ ❸ ❻)

The following information was taken from the accounting records of Cutler Inc. at December 31, 2016. Cutler Inc. is a private corporation and follows ASPE.

Line Item	Amount
Prior-year error—debit to retained earnings	$15,000
Income tax expense on operating income from discontinued operations	19,600
Total dividends	67,000
Common shares, 75,000 shares issued	201,000
Sales revenue	605,000
Interest expense	17,000
Operating income, discontinued operations	56,000
Loss due to lawsuit	16,000
Sales discounts	30,000
Income tax savings on sale of discontinued operations (sold at a loss)	8,750
General expenses	23,000
Income tax expense on continuing operations	73,150
Preferred shares, $7.00, 1,000 shares issued	60,000
Retained earnings, January 1, 2016 (prior to adjustment)	135,000
Loss on sale of assets from discontinued operations	25,000
Cost of goods sold	310,000

Assume a tax rate of 35%. During the year, no shares were issued or redeemed. Preferred dividends were paid in full.

Required

a) Prepare an income statement for the year ended December 31, 2016.

b) Prepare a statement of retained earnings for Cutler Inc. for the year ended December 31, 2016.

c) Calculate the EPS ratio.

_____

_____

_____

_____

_____

d) If Cutler Inc. had followed IFRS, what would have been the amount of other comprehensive income for the year?

_____

_____

_____

_____

_____

_____

_____

_____

Case Study

CS-1 (❷ ❸ ❹ ❺ ❻ ❼)

Kruma Company sells clothes and fashion accessories through its chain of retail stores. The shareholders' equity section of Kruma Company's statement of financial position as at December 31, 2016 shows the following information.

Kruma Company Statement of Financial Position (partial) As at December 31, 2016	
Shareholders' Equity	
Preferred Shares, non-cumulative, $3,	
100,000 shares authorized, 40,000 shares issued	$1,200,000
Common Shares, unlimited shares authorized,	
400,000 shares issued and outstanding	1,600,000
Retained Earnings	1,500,000
Total Shareholders' Equity	$4,300,000

On January 28, 2017, Kruma discovered an accounting mistake made in 2016. Accrual of interest revenue was understated by $54,000 because interest receivable and interest revenue of $60,000 were mistakenly recorded as $6,000.

During 2017, Kruma earned and incurred the following revenue and expenses (excluding income tax expenses). Kruma's tax rate is 30%.

Sales Revenue	$1,785,000
Interest Revenue	45,000
Gain on Value of Investments	12,000
Gain on Sale of Assets from Discontinued Operations	90,000
Loss on Sale of Assets from Continuing Operations	16,000
Loss on Foreign Currency Translation	30,000
Operating Loss from Discontinued Operations	200,000
Cost of Goods Sold	966,000
Salaries Expense	250,000
Depreciation Expense	174,000
Miscellaneous Operating Expenses	80,000

On October 1, 2017, Kruma issued an additional 20,000 common shares for $100,000. There was no other change in the number of common or preferred shares. Kruma paid $120,000 dividends to preferred shareholders, but no dividend to common shareholders in 2017. The preferred shares are not convertible. The company does not have any outstanding securities that can be converted into common shares.

Required

a) Record the journal entry to correct the mistake related to the understatement of interest receivable and interest revenue in 2016.

Date	Account Title and Explanation	Debit	Credit

b) Prepare an income statement under ASPE for Kruma for the year ended December 31, 2017.

c) Prepare a statement of comprehensive income by function under IFRS for Kruma for the year ended December 31, 2017. Assume that 60% and 40% of operating expenses are selling and administrative expenses respectively. Please show detailed calculations of weighted average number of common shares and earnings per share in the space provided under the statement of comprehensive income table.

Date 2017	Actual Number of Shares	Fraction of Year	Weighted Average Number of Shares

_____

_____

_____

_____

_____

_____

_____

_____

_____

_____

d) Prepare a statement of retained earnings under ASPE for Kruma for the year ended December 31, 2017.

e) Prepare a statement of changes in equity under IFRS for Kruma for the year ended December 31, 2017.

f) Prepare the shareholders' equity section of Kruma's balance sheet under ASPE as at December 31, 2017.

g) Prepare the shareholders' equity section of Kruma's statement of financial position under IFRS as at December 31, 2017.

h) In the table below, calculate the given ratios for Kruma's common shares as at December 31, 2017. Assume that the market price of Kruma's common shares on that day is equal to $4.50.

Book Value per Common Share	
Common Dividend Payout Ratio	
Price-Earnings Ratio	

Critical Thinking

CT-1 (❷ ❸ ❺ ❻ ❼)

Manipulation of financial statements by overstating revenue (or profit) and understating expenses (or costs), is one of the most common methods to commit accounting fraud. One of the famous case is WorldCom. In 2003, the company reported that it had overstated earnings and understated expenses for a total value of $74.5 billion.

One of the primary methods it used was to classify regular operating expenses as capital expenditure (also known as capital investment). By doing that, it allowed the company to amortize operating expenses over several financial periods.

Required

a) Discuss the impact this activity would have on the statement of comprehensive income and statement of financial positions, by specifying which item would be overstated or understated. Fill in your answer in the provided table.

Statement Name	Item	Overstated or Understated?
Statement of Comprehensive Income	Operational Expenses	
	Depreciation and Amortization Expenses	
	Net Income	
	Tax Expense	
	Earnings Per Share	
Statement of Financial Position	Non-Current Assets	
	Accumulated Depreciation and Amortization	
	Long-Term Investments	
	Retained Earnings	

b) Discuss what impact this activity would have on the ratios used to evaluate earnings and dividend performance, by specifying if the ratio would be overstated or understated (assuming all other factors remain unchanged).

_____

_____

_____

_____

_____

Notes

Chapter 8

NON-CURRENT LIABILITIES

―――――――――― **Assessment Questions** ――――――――――

AS-1 (❶)

Name the typical forms of non-current debt.

_____

_____

_____

AS-2 (❶)

What is a bond?

_____

_____

_____

AS-3 (❹)

An investor pays $83,333 for a bond, but will receive $100,000 when the bond matures. Has the investor bought the bond at a discount or at a premium?

_____

_____

AS-4 (❸ ❹)

Bonds can be issued at different prices relative to their face value. Name and describe the three types of bonds relative to face value.

_____

_____

_____

AS-5 (❹)

When would a bond be issued at a discount? At a premium?

_____

_____

_____

AS-6 (❹)

A $100,000 bond is issued for $110,000. Is the current market interest rate for bonds above or below the rate stated in the bond contract?

_____

_____

_____

AS-7 (❹ ❺)

What amount remains in the discount on bonds account or premium on bonds account on the maturity date of the bond?

_____

_____

_____

AS-8 (❶)

Funds raised from non-current debt are usually used for what kind of investments?

_____

_____

_____

_____

AS-9 (❶)

What are some differences between bonds and shares?

_____

_____

_____

_____

_____

_____

AS-10 (❶)

What is a term bond?

_____

_____

AS-11(❶)

What is the main difference between a debenture and a mortgage bond?

_____

_____

_____

_____

_____

_____

AS-12 (❶)

Define market interest rate.

_____

_____

_____

_____

AS-13 (❷)

If a company keeps money in a bank, the value of its money changes over time even if
nothing is done to it. What is this phenomenon called?

_____

_____

AS-14 (❷)

Peter lent $100 to his friend Angela, who promised Peter that the principal would be repaid
after two years, with 10% compound interest per annum. Two years later, Peter received $120
from Angela. Did Angela fulfill her promise to Peter? Why or why not?

_____

_____

_____

_____

_____

_____

_____

_____

_____

AS-15 (❷)

A company invested $1,000,000 to buy a property. The appraiser estimated that the property will be worth $1,500,000 in five years. Which amount is the present value of the investment and which is the future value?

_____

_____

_____

_____

_____

_____

AS-16 (❷)

What is an annuity?

_____

_____

_____

_____

_____

AS-17 (❹)

Why should a company issue callable bonds?

_____

_____

_____

_____

_____

_____

AS-18 (❻)

What is the condition that a note payable has to meet to be classified as a non-current note payable and where should it be shown on a balance sheet?

_____

_____

_____

_____

_____

_____

_____

AS-19 (❻)

What is referred to as an instalment in notes payable?

_____

_____

_____

_____

_____

_____

_____

_____

_____

_____

_____

_____

Application Questions Group A

Note: Round all calculations and final answers to the whole dollar. When needed, use the present value factors provided in the textbook.

AP-1A (❷ ❹)

On January 1, 2016, MT Biotech issued $3,500,000, 5% callable bonds due in 12 years. At the time of issue, the market interest rate is 6% (interest is due annually). Calculate the discount or premium at which the bonds were issued.

Analysis

If, after the issuance date, the market interest rate increases to 7%, how does this impact the interest expenses? Explain the impact the change in market interest rate has from the perspective of the company and of the investor.

_____

_____

_____

_____

_____

_____

_____

_____

_____

AP-2A (❸)

On September 1, 2016, Delia Company issued $264,000 worth of bonds, with an interest rate of 10% per annum. The bonds will mature on August 31, 2019. Interest will be paid annually on August 31. The company has a December 31 year-end.

Calculate the accrued interest payable on December 31, 2016.

_____

_____

_____

_____

_____

_____

_____

_____

_____

AP-3A (❸ ❺)

On April, 1, 2016, Medum Corporation issued a four-year bond worth $421,000 with an interest rate of 5% per annum. The bond was issued at par. Interest is to be paid semi-annually on September 30 and March 31, with a year-end on March 31.

Required

a) Prepare the journal entry on April 1, 2016, to issue the bonds.

Date	Account Title and Explanation	Debit	Credit

b) Prepare the journal entry on April 1, 2020, to redeem the bonds at fair value.

Date	Account Title and Explanation	Debit	Credit

AP-4A (❹)

A company issued a $500,000 bond and received $475,000 cash on February 1. Write the journal entry to record the transaction.

Date	Account Title and Explanation	Debit	Credit

AP-5A (❸)

On April 30, 2016, a company issued $600,000 worth of 4% bonds at par. The term of the bonds is 10 years, with interest payable semi-annually on October 31 and April 30. The year-end of the company is November 30. Record the journal entries related to interest for 2016 and 2017. Note that interest must be accrued at the end of each year.

Date	Account Title and Explanation	Debit	Credit

AP-6A (❷ ❹)

On January 1, 2016, Metro Inc. issued a five-year bond with a par value of $700,000. The bond bears an interest rate of 6% per annum, with the interest paid semi-annually. On January 1, 2016, the market interest rate was 8%.

Required

a) Calculate the amount of a bond discount or a bond premium.

_____

_____

_____

_____

_____

b) Prepare the journal entry to record the sale of the bonds.

Date	Account Title and Explanation	Debit	Credit

AP-7A (❸ ❺)

On February 1, 2016, Smart Water Inc. issued $500,000 worth of bonds with a 7% interest rate. The bonds were issued at par. Interest is payable semi-annually on August 1 and February 1. The bonds mature on February 1, 2026. Smart Water Inc. has a September 30 year-end.

Required

Prepare journal entries for the following.

a) the issuance of the bonds payable on February 1, 2016

b) the payment of interest on August 1, 2016

c) the required adjusting entry on September 30, 2016

d) the payment of interest on February 1, 2017

e) the maturity of the bond on February 1, 2026 assuming the interest has already been paid

Date	Account Title	Debit	Credit

AP-8A (❸ ❺)

On June 1, 2016, Glacier Inc. issued $100,000 worth of bonds with a 6% interest rate. The bonds were issued at par. Interest is payable semi-annually on December 1 and June 1. The bonds mature on June 1, 2036. Glacier Inc. has a December 31 year-end.

Required

Prepare journal entries to record the following.

a) the issuance of the bonds on June 1, 2016
b) the payment of interest on December 1, 2016
c) the required adjustment on December 31, 2016
d) the payment of interest on June 1, 2017
e) the maturity of the bonds on June 1, 2036, assuming the interest has already been paid

Date	Account Title and Explanation	Debit	Credit

AP-9A (④ ⑤)

A company is issuing $300,000 worth of five-year bonds on January 1, 2016, bearing an interest rate of 4%, payable annually. Assume that the current market rate of interest is 5%.

Required

a) Will the bond be issued at a discount or at a premium?

_____

_____

_____

_____

b) Calculate the value of the resulting discount or premium.

_____

_____

_____

_____

_____

c) Record the journal entry to reflect the sale of bonds and the appropriate discount or premium.

Date	Account Title and Explanation	Debit	Credit

d) Assuming interest is paid annually on December 31, write the journal entry to record payment of interest.

Date	Account Title and Explanation	Debit	Credit

Analysis

If, after the issuance date, the market interest rate increases to 6%, how will this change how the interest expense is recorded?

AP-10A (④)

On April 1, 2016, Hamsar Inc. issued a five-year 8% bond of $500,000 for the premium price of $542,651. Interest is to be paid semi-annually on October 1 and April 1. The company's year-end is December 31. Prepare an amortization schedule for the first four interest periods. Assume the market rate of interest was 6% on the issuance date.

Semi-Annual Interest Period	A Interest Payment	B Interest Expense	C Premium Amortization	D Bond Amortized Cost

Analysis

Would the total cash payment for interest be different from the total interest expenses recorded over the term of the bonds? Explain.

_____

_____

_____

_____

_____

_____

AP-11A (④ ⑦)

Burroughs Corporation (with a December 31 year-end) issued $450,000, 9.5% bonds due in eight years on May 1, 2016. Interest is paid semi-annually on November 1 and May 1 of each year. On the issuance date, the market rate of interest was 8.5%, resulting in a price of $475,746 for these bonds.

Note: The premium/discount is amortized using the effective interest method.

a) Is this bond issued at a discount or at a premium? Prepare the journal entry on May 1, 2016, to record the issue of the bonds.

_____

_____

Date	Account Title and Explanation	Debit	Credit

b) Prepare the journal entry on November 1, 2016, to record the first interest payment and the amortization of the premium/discount.

Date	Account Title and Explanation	Debit	Credit

c) Prepare the adjusting entry on December 31, 2016.

Date	Account Title and Explanation	Debit	Credit

d) Show the balance sheet presentation of Bonds Payable and related accounts as at December 31, 2016.

AP-12A (❷❹❺)

Fountain Hills Corporation is planning to build a new arena for the community. To complete the project, the company is issuing $3,000,000 worth of five-year, 10% bonds with interest paid semi-annually.

On May 1, 2016, the company completed all the necessary paperwork and is now ready to issue the bonds. The market rate on the date of issuance is 8%. The company uses the effective interest method to amortize any premiums or discounts.

Required

Record journal entries for the following items. Round all amounts to the nearest whole dollar.

a) The issuance of the bond on May 1, 2016 (Hint: This will require the calculation of the premium/discount).
b) The payment of interest on October 31, 2016.
c) The necessary adjusting entries at the company's December 31, 2016 year-end.
d) The payment of interest on April 30, 2017.
e) The retirement of the bonds on May 1, 2021 (assume interest has already been paid).

Date	Account Title and Explanation	Debit	Credit

AP-13A (❷ ❹ ❺)

Wilson Corp. is planning to build a new tennis court for the community. To complete the project, the company is issuing $1,000,000 worth of five-year, 10% bonds with interest paid semi-annually.

On May 1, 2016, the company issued the bonds. The market rate on the date of issuance was 12%.

Required

Record journal entries for the following items. Use the effective interest method to amortize any premiums/discounts. Round all amounts to the nearest whole dollar.

a) The issuance of the bond on May 1, 2016.
b) The payment of interest on October 31, 2016.
c) The necessary adjusting entries at the company's December 31, 2016 year end.
d) The payment of interest on April 30, 2017.
e) The retirement of the bonds on May 1, 2021 (assume interest has already been paid).

Date	Account Title and Explanation	Debit	Credit

AP-14A (❷ ❹)

On July 1, 2016, Marky Corporation issued $1,500,000 worth of bonds with 9% interest rate. Interest is payable semi-annually on June 30 and December 31. The bonds mature on June 30, 2023. At the time of the bond issuance, the market interest rate was 8%. Any discount or premium resulting from the sale of the bonds will be amortized using the effective interest method. The company's year-end is March 31.

Required

a) Calculate the total price of the bonds on the issue date and determine the amount of a bond discount or a bond premium.

_____

_____

_____

_____

_____

_____

b) Prepare the journal entries to record the issuance of the bond and the first interest payment.

Date	Account Title and Explanation	Debit	Credit

c) Prepare the journal entry required on March 31, 2017.

Date	Account Title and Explanation	Debit	Credit

d) Prepare the journal entry required on June 30, 2017.

Date	Account Title and Explanation	Debit	Credit

e) Calculate the book value (carrying amount) of bonds payable at December 31, 2016.

_____

_____

_____

_____

_____

AP-15A (❼)

On January 1, 2015, Sedar Co. issued a five-year, 8% instalment notes payable for $120,000 to finance upgrading its current equipment. The company's year-end is December 31. The repayment is done semi-annually on January 1 and July 1. Use a fixed principal plus interest method to show the current and non-current liabilities on the partial balance sheet as at December 31, 2017. Assume no other non-current liability has occurred, and accounts payable and interest payable have balances of $50,000 and $2,400 respectively on December 31, 2017.

Analysis

Compare the total interest expenses incurred under the fixed principal and blended payment methods for Sedar Co. Assume an equal instalment amount of $14,795 per interest period for the blended method. Which one produces a greater amount of interest over five years?

_____

_____

_____

_____

_____

_____

_____

_____

_____

_____

_____

_____

_____

_____

_____

_____

_____

_____

_____

_____

_____

_____

_____

_____

_____

_____

_____

_____

_____

_____

_____

_____

_____

_____

_____

AP-16A (⑥)

Evans Ltd. decides to issue a three-year, $150,000 note payable on January 1, 2016 to finance the purchase of lab equipment, with an interest rate of 6%. The repayment is done annually on its year-end date of December 31.

Required

a) How much will Evans Ltd. have to pay back at the end of 2016, 2017 and 2018 if the fixed principal plus interest method is used?

Date	A Cash Payment	B Interest Expense	C Reduction of Principal	D Principal Balance
Jan 1, 2016				
Dec 31, 2016				
Dec 31, 2017				
Dec 31, 2018				

b) Prepare journal entries to record issuing the note payable and all payments for 2016, 2017 and 2018.

Date	Account Titles and Explanations	Debit	Credit

AP-17A (6)

Aidan's Inc. is looking to replace its old delivery truck, which constantly breaks down. It just happens that one of its suppliers has a slightly used delivery truck for sale. Because Aidan's Inc. has been doing business with this supplier for many years, the supplier offers Aidan's a great deal.

The supplier will sell the truck to Aidan's for $68,000 on January 1, 2016 and issue a five-year note payable at 3%. Instalment payments of $7,374 are made semi-annually.

Prepare a table to calculate the total interest paid over the life of the note.

Round all amounts to the nearest whole dollar.

	A	B	C	D
Date	Cash Payment	Interest Expense	Reduction of Principal	Principal Balance

_____

_____

_____

_____

_____

_____

Application Questions Group B

Note: Round all calculations and final answers to whole dollar. When needed, use the present value factors provided in the textbook.

AP-1B (❷ ❹)

On January 1, 2016, Bootic Inc. issued $3,500,000, 6% callable bonds due in 12 years. At the time of issue, the market interest rate is 5% (interest is due annually). Calculate the discount or premium at which the bonds were issued. The company's year-end is December 31.

AP-2B (❸)

On April 1, 2016, Dixon Company issued $300,000 worth of bonds, with the interest rate of 12% per annum. The bonds will mature on March 31, 2023. Interest will be paid semi-annually on September 30 and March 31. The company has a December 31 year-end. Calculate the accrued interest payable on December 31, 2017.

AP-3B (❸)

A company issued $502,000 of bonds at par on July 4, 2016. Write the journal entry to record the transaction.

Date	Account Title and Explanation	Debit	Credit

AP-4B (❹)

A company issued a $500,000 bond and received $525,000 cash on August 1, 2016. Write the journal entry to record the transaction.

Date	Account Title and Explanation	Debit	Credit

AP-5B (❸)

On April 30, 2016, a company issued $588,000 worth of 9% bonds at par. The term of the bonds is seven years, with interest payable semi-annually on October 31 and April 30. The year-end of the company is November 30. Record the journal entries related to interest for 2016 and 2017. Note that interest must be accrued at the end of each year.

Date	Account Title and Explanation	Debit	Credit

AP-6B (❹)

On July 1, 2016, Dilly Company received $562,316 cash for the sale of a 10-year bond with a face value of $500,000. The bond bears an interest rate of 12%, to be paid semi-annually. At the time of the sale, the market interest rate was 10%. The year-end is December 31. Prepare a journal entry to record the issuance of bond.

Date	Account Title and Explanation	Debit	Credit

AP-7B (❸ ❺)

On May 1, 2016, Sweet Lily Flower Inc. issued $30,000 worth of bonds with a 5% interest rate. The bonds were issued at par. Interest is payable semi-annually on November 1 and May 1. The bonds mature on May 1, 2026. Sweet Lily Flower Inc. has a December 31 year-end.

Required

Prepare the journal entries to record the following.

a) The issuance of the bonds payable on May 1, 2016.

b) The payment of interest on November 1, 2016.

c) The required adjusting entry on December 31, 2016.

d) The payment of interest on May 1, 2017.

e) The maturity of the bond on May 1, 2026 assuming the interest has already been paid.

Date	Account Title	Debit	Credit

AP-8B (❸ ❺)

On November 1, 2016, Breyer Inc. issued $800,000 worth of bonds with a 9% interest rate. The bonds were issued at par. Interest is payable annually on October 31. The bonds mature on October 31, 2026. Breyer Inc. has a December 31 year-end.

Required

Prepare the necessary journal entries to record the following.

a) The issuance of the bonds payable on November 1, 2016.
b) The required adjustment on December 31, 2016.
c) The payment of interest on October 31, 2017.
d) The maturity of the bond on October 31, 2026 with interest.

Date	Account Title and Explanation	Debit	Credit

AP-9B (❷ ❸ ❹)

A company issued $1,200,000 worth of 15-year bonds with a 3% interest rate. Interest is to be paid annually. The bond issue date is January 1, 2016 and the company has a year-end of December 31.

Required

a) Calculate the bond issue price under each market interest rate.

Market Interest Rate	Bond Price
2%	
3%	
4%	

_____

_____

_____

_____

_____

_____

_____

_____

_____

_____

_____

_____

_____

_____

_____

_____

_____

_____

_____

b) For each market condition, prepare a journal entry to record the bond issuance.

Market Interest Rate—2%

Date	Account Title and Explanation	Debit	Credit

Market Interest Rate—3%

Date	Account Title and Explanation	Debit	Credit

Market Interest Rate—4%

Date	Account Title and Explanation	Debit	Credit

AP-10B (❹)

On July 1, 2016, Den Inc. issued a seven-year, 10% bond of $500,000 for the discount price of $453,525. Interest is to be paid semi-annually on June 30 and December 31. The company's year-end is July 31. Prepare an amortization schedule for the first four interest periods. Assume the market rate of interest was 12% on the issuance date.

Semi-Annual Interest Period	A Interest Payment	B Interest Expense	C Premium Amortization	D Bond Amortized Cost

Analysis

Explain if the total cash payment for interest would be different from the total interest expenses recorded over the term of the bonds in this question.

_____

_____

_____

_____

_____

_____

_____

_____

_____

_____

_____

_____

AP-11B (❶ ❼)

Sam's Construction is a construction company (with a December 31 year-end) that is planning to expand its facilities by constructing a new building, and acquiring new equipment. To complete this project, the company has decided to issue $100,000 worth of 10-year bonds at 5% on March 1, 2016. The interest payment is made semi-annually on September 1 and March 1. Just as the company completes all the necessary contracts, and is ready to issue the bonds, the market rate increases to 6%, resulting in a price of $92,564 for these bonds.

Note: The premium/discount is amortized using the effective interest method.

Required

a) Are these bonds issued at a discount or at a premium? Prepare the journal entry for the issuance of bonds on March 1, 2016.

Date	Account Title and Explanation	Debit	Credit

b) Prepare the journal entry for the first payment of interest on September 1, 2016.

Date	Account Title and Explanation	Debit	Credit

c)   Prepare the adjusting entry on December 31, 2016.

Date	Account Title and Explanation	Debit	Credit

d)   Show the balance sheet presentation of Bonds Payable and related accounts as at
     December 31, 2016.

AP-12B (❷ ❹ ❺)

Phillips Corporation is planning to expand into a new product line. To do this, the company has decided to issue $200,000 worth of five-year, 6% bonds with interest paid annually.

On June 1, 2016, the company completed all the necessary paperwork and is now ready to issue the bonds. The market rate on the date of issuance is 5%. Use the effective interest method to amortize any premiums/discounts.

Required

Record the journal entries for the following items. Round all amounts to the nearest whole dollar.

a) The issuance of the bond on June 1, 2016 (Hint: This will require the calculation of the premium/discount).
b) The necessary adjusting entries at the company's December 31, 2016 year-end.
c) The payment of interest on May 31, 2017.
d) The retirement of the bonds on June 1, 2021 (assume interest has already been paid).

Date	Account Title and Explanation	Debit	Credit

AP-13B (❷ ❹ ❺)

Watson Corporation is planning to expand into a new product line. To complete the expansion, the company has decided to issue $200,000 worth of five-year, 3% bonds with interest paid annually.

On June 1, 2016, the company issued the bonds. The market rate on the date of issuance was 4%. Use the effective interest method to amortize any premiums/discounts.

Required

Record the journal entries for the following items. Round all amounts to the nearest whole dollar.

a) The issuance of the bond on June 1, 2016 (Hint: This will require the calculation of the premium/discount).
b) The necessary adjusting entries at the company's December 31, 2016 year-end.
c) The payment of interest on May 31, 2017.
d) The retirement of the bonds on June 1, 2021 (assume interest has already been paid).

Date	Account Title and Explanation	Debit	Credit

AP-14B (❶ ❺)

On May 1, 2016, Ezzy Company issued a six-year bond worth $400,000 with an interest rate of 8% per annum. Interest is to be paid semi-annually on October 31 and April 30. At the time of the issuance, the market interest rate was 6%. Ezzy Company amortizes any premium or discount using the effective interest method.

Required

a) Calculate the bond issue price and the resulting premium or discount.

_____

_____

_____

_____

_____

b) Prepare journal entries to record the following bonds payable transactions.

1) Issuance of bonds on May 1, 2016.
2) Payment of interest and amortization of premium on October 31, 2016.
3) Accrual of interest and amortization of premium on December 31, 2016, which is the company's year-end.
4) Payment of interest and amortization of premium on April 30, 2017.
5) Redemption of the bond for $406,000 on May 1, 2021 (one year before maturity).

Date	Account Title and Explanation	Debit	Credit

Date	Account Title and Explanation	Debit	Credit

AP-15B (❼)

On December 31, 2016, Shima Company issued a four-year, 12% instalment notes payable for $400,000 to finance an additional product line. The company's year-end is December 31. The repayment is done quarterly starting from March 31. Using a blended payment plus interest method, present how the current and non-current sections for this notes payable would be shown on the partial balance sheet as of December 31, 2017. Assume an equal instalment amount of $31,844 is determined per quarter.

_____

_____

_____

_____

_____

_____

_____

_____

_____

_____

_____

_____

_____

_____

Analysis

If Shima Company is experiencing some cash flow problems and would like to minimize initial interest payments, would you recommend the company to use blended payment method or fixed principal payment method for managing its notes payable overall?

_____

_____

_____

_____

_____

_____

_____

_____

AP-16B (❻)

On January 1, 2016, Hala Ltd. issued a three-year, $150,000 note payable to finance the purchase of factory equipment, with an interest rate of 6%. The repayment is done annually on December 31.

Required

a) How much principal will Hala Ltd. pay back at the end of 2016, 2017 and 2018, if the blended principal plus interest method is used? Assume an equal instalment amount of $56,117 is determined per year.

Date	A	B	C	D
	Cash Payment	**Interest Expense**	**Reduction of Principal**	**Principal Balance**

b) Prepare journal entries from January 1 to December 31, 2016. Assume the company's year-end is June 30.

Date	Account Titles and Explanations	Debit	Credit

AP-17B (⊙)

Bee Inc. needs a truck for its current operations. The company just received a good deal from one of its long-time clients.

The client will sell the truck to Bee for $68,000 on January 1, 2016 and issue a five-year note payable at 6%. Payments will be made semi-annually using the fixed principal plus interest.

Prepare a table to calculate the total interest paid over the life of the note.

Round all amounts to the nearest whole dollar.

Interest Payable	A Cash Payment	B Interest Expense	C Reduction of Principal	D Principal Balance

Case Study

CS-1 (❶ ❼)

You & Us Company issued a callable six-year, $1,000,000 bond on December 1, 2013. The interest rate was 4% per year and interest payment would be made semi-annually. In 2013, similar bonds were paying 6% interest on average.

On December 1, 2016, the average market interest rate for similar bonds had decreased to 2%. You & Us Company decided to redeem all the outstanding bonds issued in 2013 and issue new bonds. The new bonds will also have an annual interest rate of 4%. You & Us Company's fiscal year-end is on December 31.

In 2013, You & Us Company hired a bookkeeper, who did not have a professional accounting designation. The bookkeeper recorded the journal entries for the issuance of the bond and the two payments of interest in 2014, which are all shown below.

Date	Account Titles and Explanations	Debit	Credit
Dec 1, 2013	Cash	900,480	
	Discount on Bonds	99,520	
	Bonds Payable		1,000,000
	To record issuing of $1,000,000 bonds at discount		
Dec 31, 2013	No journal entry on issued bonds		
Jun 1, 2014	Interest Expense	20,000	
	Cash		20,000
	To record interest payment on bonds		
Dec 1, 2014	Interest Expense	20,000	
	Cash		20,000
	Record interest payment on bonds		
Dec 31, 2014	No journal entry on issued bonds		

Required

a) In January 2015, an auditor found errors relating to the bond transactions from 2013 and
    2014. What adjustment is required to correct those errors, and what is the correct balance
    on the discount on bonds account?

Date	A Cash Payment	B Interest Expense	C Reduction of Principal	D Principal Balance

_____

_____

_____

_____

_____

_____

b) Calculate the value of the new bond issued on December 1, 2016 to replace the bond
    issued in 2013. The new three-year $1,000,000 bonds pay 4% interest annually. The current
    market rate is 2%.

_____

_____

_____

_____

_____

_____

Critical Thinking

CT-1 (❷ ❹)

When it comes to bonds, IFRS requires using the effective interest method while ASPE allows the straight-line method if the results do not differ significantly. Which method do you recommend for a private company following ASPE? Support your answer.

_____

_____

_____

_____

_____

_____

_____

_____

_____

_____

_____

_____

_____

_____

_____

_____

_____

_____

_____

_____

_____

Chapter 9

INVESTMENTS

Assessment Questions

AS-1 (❶)

How is a short-term investment different from a long-term investment? Name a few short-term investments.

_____

_____

_____

_____

_____

_____

_____

_____

_____

_____

AS-2 (❶ ❹)

Explain how long-term investments are classified on a balance sheet. Name a few long-term investments.

_____

_____

_____

_____

_____

AS-3 (❶)

Ava Company issues 10-year, $1,000,000 term bonds paying 3% semi-annual interests. Bea Company purchased 20% of these term bonds on the issuance date. Which company is the investor and which company is the investee?

_____

_____

AS-4 (❶)

Sometimes terms are used such as debt or equity instruments versus debt or equity securities. What is the difference between a security and an instrument?

_____

_____

_____

AS-5 (❶)

Zed Company, a public company, is planning to invest in a 20-year debt security for the purpose of selling it within six months to make a profit. Which method should Zed Company use for accounting of this investment?

_____

_____

_____

AS-6 (❶)

Shu Company follows ASPE and it is planning to invest in a 20-year debt security for the purpose of selling it within six months to make a profit. Which method should Shu Company use for accounting of this investment?

_____

_____

_____

AS-7 (❶)

YAL Inc. is planning to invest in a 20-year debt security with the intention to hold it until maturity and receive interest revenue. Would YAL Inc. classify this debt security as a strategic investment or non-strategic investment?

_____

_____

_____

AS-8 (❶)

X Company is planning to purchase 100,000 (or 5%) common shares of a US company to alleviate some of the risks related to the exchange rate fluctuations between US dollars and Canadian dollars. Which method should X Company use for accounting of this investment?

_____

_____

_____

AS-9 (❶)

LINIX Company is planning to purchase 100,000 (or 25%) common shares of another company for the purpose of trading. Which method should LINIX Company use for accounting of this investment?

_____

_____

_____

AS-10 (❷)

What is a trading investment? Is it a debt or equity investment?

_____

_____

_____

AS-11 (❷)

Why are money market instruments, such as a treasury bill (T-bill), term deposit or money market fund considered short-term debt instruments ?

_____

_____

_____

AS-12 (❷)

The amortized cost method can be used to record short-term investment of treasury bills (T-bills). Why do you think using the amortized cost method to record a 90-day T-bill investment is appropriate?

_____

_____

_____

_____

_____

_____

_____

_____

_____

AS-13 (❶)

On January 1, 2016, Meltam Company purchased 30% of the outstanding common shares of another company at $65 per share. The investment has given Meltam significant influence. At year-end, the price has gone up to $67.00 per share. How should the company record this price adjustment?

_____

_____

_____

_____

_____

AS-14 (❷)

The fair value through profit and loss method can be used to record both debt investments and equity investments. What kind of debt and equity investments can be recorded using this method?

_____

_____

_____

_____

AS-15 (❸)

Determine the level of influence that the investor has over the investee at 7%, 21% and 51% of the ownership.

Percentage of Ownership by Investor	Investor's Level of Influence on Investee
7%	
21%	
51%	

AS-16 (❷ ❸ ❹)

Discuss the main difference between fair value method and the fair value through profit and loss method.

_____

_____

_____

_____

_____

_____

AS-17 (❸)

Under the equity method, net profit from the investee company is recorded proportionately as part of the investment revenue for the investor. When the investor company receives cash dividend from the investee, which account should be credited?

_____

_____

_____

_____

_____

AS-18 (❸)

Under what circumstances should the cost method be used for recording equity investments?

_____

_____

_____

_____

Application Questions Group A

AP-1A (❶)

Affy Company makes some investments in 2016. Affy Company has adopted IFRS standards since 2011. Complete the following table for each of the investments.

Investments	Non-Strategic or Strategic Investment	Classification on Affy Company's Balance Sheet	Accounting Treatment
A 90-day treasury bill purchased on November 15, 2016 that Affy plans to hold for interest revenue until maturity.			
A two-year provincial bond purchased on April 1, 2016 that Affy is planning to sell before the year-end of December 31, 2016.			
A five-year bond issued by a private business on November 1, 2016 that Affy is planning to hold until maturity.			
10% of common shares of Smith Company purchased on November 2, 2016 with significant influence over the investee.			
6% of common shares of John Company purchased on December 2, 2016, which Affy is planning to hold for a short period of time before selling to make a profit.			
45% of common shares of Steve Company, with which Affy has just signed a long-term business alliance agreement.			

AP-2A (❶ ❷)

Kaman Company is a public company. It decided to purchase a $200,000, 90-day treasury bill (T-bill) on March 1, 2016 for $198,046. The investment will mature on May 29, 2016. Kaman plans to hold this investment until maturity. The market rate for this type of T-bill is set at 4% annually. The company's year-end is March 31.

Round your answers to the nearest whole dollar.

Required

a) What kind of accounting methods should be considered to record this investment?

_____

_____

_____

b) Prepare journal entries for the acquisition, year end and maturity date.

Date	Account Title and Explanation	Debit	Credit

AP-3A (❶ ❷)

Feng Inc. is planning to purchase $250,000 worth of six-year bonds issued by George Company, a publically traded company in Ontario, on January 1, 2016 for $236,782. The interest rate of the bonds is 3% annually; payments are made semi-annually on June 30 and December 31 every year. The interest rate paid by similar bonds is at 4% per year in the market. Feng Inc. has a December 31 year-end.

Required

a) If Feng's investment goal is to hold the bonds to collect interest revenue, which valuation method should be used in recording these bonds?

_____

_____

_____

b) Prepare journal entries for the bonds' acquisition, the first and last interest payments and retirement of the bonds on January 1, 2022.

Date	Account Title and Explanation	Debit	Credit

AP-4A (❶❷)

Jenny Company, a public company, purchases a 120-day, $5,000,000 Canadian Government T-bill on March 1, 2016, with a cash payment of $4,975,463. The T-bill pays 1.5% per year. As part of the recent investment strategies, Jenny Company decided to make the best use of its idle cash to earn extra profit. The company might sell this T-bill at any time before the maturity date, should the market situation turn favourable. Assume that Jenny Company has a year-end date of April 30.

Required

a) Which accounting method is most appropriate to record this investment and why?

_____

_____

_____

_____

_____

b) Prepare journal entries for the purchase and year-end accrual.

Date	Account Title and Explanation	Debit	Credit

AP-5A (❶ ❷)

On July 1, 2016, Kabir Company, a public company, decided to buy $240,000, 6% 10-year bonds at par, issued by a private company in Canada. The semi-annual payments are made on January 1 and July 1. The company intends to trade the bonds within the next six to nine months. Kabir Company records the bonds using the fair value through profit and loss method, in compliance with IFRS. Kabir Company has a year-end of September 30.

Required

a) Record acquisition of the bonds.

Date	Account Title and Explanation	Debit	Credit

b) Assume that on September 30, 2016, the market value of the bonds decreased significantly to $219,000 due to a change of market interest rate. Prepare journal entries to make the adjustment on this date. You do not need to record the interest accrued for this question.

Date	Account Title and Explanation	Debit	Credit

AP-6A (❶ ❷)

Midland Company's investment activities from 2016 to 2017 are recorded below. Its year-end is on December 31.

1) On January 21, 2016, Midland Company purchased 200 common shares of Yahoo Holding from Toronto Stock Exchange at $18.92 per share. The equity instrument is purchased for the purpose of trading.
2) On June 30, 2016, Midland Company received dividends from Yahoo Holding of $1.50 per share.
3) On December 31, 2016, the trading price of Yahoo Holding went up to $19.00 per share.
4) On January 28, 2017, Midland Company sold all 200 Yahoo Holding shares at $19.23 per share.

Record journal entries of the provided investment activities for Midland Company.

Date	Account Title and Explanation	Debit	Credit

AP-7A (❶ ❸)

To expand further into the market, on January 2, 2016, Oliver Company purchased 150,000 common shares of Provide Company, a public company with 1,000,000 outstanding common shares traded on the Toronto Stock Exchange.

Required

a) What level of influence does Oliver Company have over Provide Company solely based on the percentage of ownership? Which accounting method should be considered for recording this investment?

_____

_____

_____

_____

_____

b) At minimum, how many shares need to be acquired by Oliver Company for significant influence to be exercised?

_____

_____

_____

AP-8A (❶ ❸)

On March 2, 2016, Taxes Holding, a public company, purchased 15% of the 2,000,000 outstanding common shares issued by Utah Holding at a price of $28.75 per share. This investment occurred as part of a business alliance agreement between the two companies. Taxes Holding is planning to hold on to those common shares of Utah Holding for at least 10 years if not longer.

During 2016, the following activities occurred in regards to this investment.

1) On June 30, 2016, Taxes Holding received a cash dividend from Utah Holding for $1.36 per share.

2) On December 31, 2016, the year-end date of Taxes Holding, Utah Holding common shares were traded at $29.02 per share.

Required

a) Which accounting method should be chosen in this situation and why?

_____

_____

_____

b) Prepare journal entries to record the acquisition of Utah Holding's common shares, receipt of cash dividends and year-end adjustments related to Utah Holding's investment in Taxes Holding's books.

Date	Account Title and Explanation	Debit	Credit

AP-9A (❸)

On May 1, 2016, Xiao Company, a public company, acquired 210,000 of the 600,000 outstanding common shares from Zahra Company for a total of $1,680,000. This investment is part of Xiao Company's long-term business diversification plan. Xiao Company's year-end is December 31. During 2016, the following investment activities occurred.

1) Zahra Company recorded an annual net income of $908,000 for its 2015–2016 fiscal year-end of June 30, 2016.

2) Zahra Company paid a cash dividend of $300,000 on July 30, 2016.

Required

a) Prepare journal entries to record the acquisition of the 210,000 common shares by Xiao Company.

b) Prepare journal entries to record revenue of investment from Zahra Company on June 30, 2016.

c) Prepare journal entries to record the receipt of cash dividends on July 30, 2016.

Date	Account Title and Explanation	Debit	Credit

AP-10A (❸)

Candy Company purchased 25% of David Company's 400,000 common shares outstanding, on March 1, 2016. Candy Company paid $3.00 per share. Candy Company is considered to have significant influence over David Company and applies the cost method for recording this investment. Candy Company's year-end is on December 31. The company follows ASPE.

Required

a) Prepare journal entries for the acquisition of David Company's common shares by Candy Company.

b) Prepare journal entries for the $15,000 dividends received from David Company on December 31, 2016.

c) On January 1, 2017, Candy Company sold 5% of David Company's common shares for $5.00 per share. Prepare the journal entries for this transaction.

Date	Account Title and Explanation	Debit	Credit

AP-11A (❶)

Different accounting methods of recording investments impact different accounts in either the balance sheet or income statement. From a list of transactions given below, indicate how each account is impacted for the investor. The first one is completed for you as an example.

Item No.	Transaction
1	The $300 interest accrued on a 90-day T-bill.
2	Interest receipt in cash of $4,800 with interest revenue of $4,300 from a long-term investment bond.
3	Sale of a long-term investment bond for $10,300 cash before maturity, with a book value of $10,900.
4	Accrued interest revenue of $520 for a non-strategic long-term bond investment at year-end.
5	An adjustment of a market price increase of $900 for a non-strategic long-term bond investment.
6	The $3,000 cash dividend received from the equity investment recorded using the fair value method.
7	Fair value increase of an equity investment for $1,500. The investment is valued based on the cost method.
8	The $1,200 cash dividend received for a strategic equity investment using the equity method.
9	The fair value increase of $3,300 for a long-term investment in common shares recorded using the fair value method.
10	Using the equity method, an associate company reported $100,000 of net profit. The investor owns 35% of an associate's common shares.

	Income Statement			Balance Sheet	
	Revenue	Expense	OCI	Current Assets	Non-Current Assets
Item No.					
1	+$300			+$300	
2					
3					
4					
5					
6					
7					
8					
9					
10					

AP-12A (❶ ❷ ❸)

Ian Company, a public company, had the following activities related to its investments over the course of two years. It has a year-end of December 31.

1) On January 31, 2016, it acquired 6% of the 1,000,000 outstanding common shares of James Company, for the purpose of short-term trading, at $16.00 per share

2) On December 31, 2016, Ian Company received a cash dividend from James Company of $1.50 per share

3) On December 31, 2016, James Company's common shares were traded at $16.50 per share on the local stock exchange

4) On January 1, 2017, Ian Company purchased 25% of the 800,000 Lemon Inc.'s outstanding common shares for a price of $1,100,000. This purchase was enough to give Ian Company significant influence over Lemon Inc.'s operational decisions.

5) On December 31, 2017, Ian Company received a cash dividend payment of $1.50 per share from James Company and $0.50 from Lemon Inc. James Company and Lemon Inc. also reported earnings of $500,000 and $650,000, respectively, for 2017.

6) On December 31, 2017, the shares of James Company and Lemon Inc. were trading at $14.00 and $4, respectively.

Required

a) Discuss which accounting method should be used by Ian Company for each type of investment.

_____

_____

_____

_____

_____

_____

_____

_____

b) Prepare journal entries of all activities recorded by Ian Company.

Date	Account Title and Explanation	Debit	Credit

AP-13A (❶ ❸)

The following are investment activities for Koko Company. Assume the company follows IFRS.

1) On January 31, 2016, Koko Company purchased a $20,000, 10-year bond at par with 5% interest paid annually on December 31. Koko Company is planning to hold this investment until maturity.

2) On February 10, 2016, Koko Company invested $15,000 in Bast Company by purchasing 3,000 common shares. Koko Company is planning to sell these shares to make a profit before the end of the year.

3) On March 1, 2016, Koko Company made a strategic business investment of $62,500 with Engrid Company by acquiring 5% of its 100,000 outstanding common shares.

4) On April 1, 2016, Koko Company received a cash dividend from Bast Company for a total of $900.

5) On April 30, 2016, Koko Company received a cash dividend from Engrid Company for a total of $1,250.

6) On Koko Company's year-end of October 31, 2016, Bast Company's common shares were trading at $6.00 per share, and Engrid Company's shares were trading at $12.15 per share.

Required

a) Prepare journal entries using proper accounting methods for all transactions including the year-end accrual of bonds' interest.

Date	Account Title and Explanation	Debit	Credit

b) Assume that on March 1, 2016, Koko Company followed ASPE and purchased 40% of Engrid Company's common shares instead of 5% (i.e. 40,000 common shares). Koko paid $500,000 for these shares and uses the cost method to account for significant influence. Prepare the journal entries required from March 1 to October 31, 2016. Adjust the dividends received for 40% of ownership.

Date	Account Title and Explanation	Debit	Credit

AP-14A (❸)

On January 1, 2016, PUT Company acquired 40% of the 800,000 outstanding common shares from SIMA Company and paid $3,500,000 in cash. On July 1, 2016, SIMA Company reported a profit of $830,000 on its annual financial statements ending June 30, 2016. SIMA Company paid cash dividends of $0.68 per common share on July 30, 2016. PUT Company is a private company that follows ASPE standards. However, it is considering to adopt IFRS standards in the near future. The CEO wants to know how much of a difference net income can be if it uses IFRS standards instead (equity method). Calculate the difference in net income for the CEO, showing your calculation of income under each method.

AP-15A (❸)

Raj Company had the following activities in relation to its investments in 2016. The company follows IFRS with June 30 as its year-end.

1) On January 1, 2016, Raj purchased 25,000 (or 25%) common shares from Terry Company for $960,000.

2) On March 31, 2016, Raj Company's accountant received financial statements from Terry Company, which reported a net profit of $386,000 for the year ending February 28, 2016.

3) On April 30, 2016, Raj Company received cash dividends from Terry Company of $1.10 per share.

4) On June 30, 2016, Raj Company's year-end, Terry Company's shares were traded at $39.20 per share.

Required

a) Prepare journal entries to record the above activities assuming significant influence is **not** achieved.

Date	Account Title and Explanation	Debit	Credit

b) Prepare journal entries to record the above activities assuming significant influence is achieved.

Date	Account Title and Explanation	Debit	Credit

Analysis

If Raj Company had purchased the common shares of Terry Company for trading purposes, Raj was then NOT allowed to classify the investment as a long-term investment. Why would IFRS enforce this type of restrictions on recording investments?

_____

_____

_____

_____

_____

_____

_____

_____

_____

Application Questions Group B

AP-1B (❶)

Betty Company invests in different instruments before the end of 2016. Complete the following table for each of the investments.

Investments	Non-Strategic or Strategic Investment	Classification on Betty Company's Balance Sheet	Accounting Method
120-day treasury bill purchased on December 31, 2016 that Betty plans to hold for interest revenue until maturity.			
A 3% common shares of a public company purchased on February 1, 2016 that Betty Company is planning on selling before the year-end of December 31, 2016.			
A one-year bond issued by a private business on November 1, 2016 that Betty Company is planning to hold until maturity.			
20% of common shares of Tim Company purchased on November 18, 2016. Currently, the company has significant influence over the investee.			
15% of common shares of Jerry Company purchased on December 24, 2016, which Betty is planning to sell within five months to make a profit.			
45% of common shares of Sally Company purchased on December 30, 2016, with which Betty Company is trying to acquire more shares to establish control over the investee in the future.			

AP-2B (❶ ❷)

Quest Company purchases a $350,000, 120-day treasury bill (T-bill) on March 1, 2016 for $344,339 in cash. The treasury bill pays 5% interest. Quest plans to hold the T-bill until maturity to earn interest. The company follows IFRS and its year-end is April 30.

Round your answers to the nearest whole dollar.

Required

a) If the accountant of Quest Company decides to use fair value through profit and loss methods, would you agree with this? Explain.

b) Prepare journal entries for the acquisition, year-end and maturity date.

Date	Account Title and Explanation	Debit	Credit

AP-3B (❶ ❷)

To earn some additional interest revenue, Hank Company, a public company, purchased $200,000 worth of 8%, five-year bonds issued by Ivy Company on January 1, 2016. Interest payments are made semi-annually on June 30 and December 31 every year. The interest rate paid by similar bonds is at 4% per year in the market as of January 2016. Assume April 30 is the year-end for Hank Company.

Required

a) Will Hank Company purchase the bonds at a discount or a premium? Use present value calculation to support your answer.

_____

_____

_____

b) Prepare journal entries for the acquisition of the bonds, the interest accrual on the first year-end, the first and last cash receipts of interest, and the cash receipt of principal at maturity on January 1, 2021.

Date	Account Title and Explanation	Debit	Credit

Date	Account Title and Explanation	Debit	Credit

Analysis

If the same bonds were traded at a discount in 2017 due to the significant increase of interest rate in the market, should Hank Company change the valuation methods of these bonds? Why or why not?

_____

_____

_____

_____

_____

AP-4B (❶ ❷)

Jimmy Company, a public company, purchases a 120-day, $5,000,000 Canadian Government T-bill on April 1, 2016, when the market interest rate is 6%. Jimmy pays $4,903,277 for the T-bill. The company plans to sell this T-bill at any time before the maturity date, should the market situation turn favourable. Assume that Jimmy Company has a year-end date of April 30.

Assume Jimmy Company sold the 120-day, $5,000,000 T-bill for $4,940,000 on May 1, 2016. Prepare journal entries for the purchase, accruals of interest at the year-end and sale of the T-bill.

Date	Account Title and Explanation	Debit	Credit

Analysis

Do you think Jimmy Company made the right decision to sell this T-bill on May 1, 2016? Explain.

_____

_____

_____

AP-5B (❶ ❷)

On July 1, 2016, Landmark Company, a public company, decided to buy $140,000 worth of 10-year bonds at par with an annual interest rate of 7%, issued by a private company. Interest is paid semi-annually on January 1 and July 1. The company intends to trade the bonds within the next two years. Landmark Company records the bonds using fair value through profit and loss method. The company's year-end is on November 30.

Required

a) Record acquisition of the bonds.

Date	Account Title and Explanation	Debit	Credit

b) Assume that on November 30, 2016, the market value of the bonds increased to $145,000 due to a change of market interest rate. Prepare journal entries to make the adjustment on this date. You do not need to record the interest accrued for this question.

Date	Account Title and Explanation	Debit	Credit

AP-6B (❶ ❷)

Norman Company's investment activities from 2016 to 2017 are recorded below. Its year-end is on December 31.

1) On January 21, 2016, Norman Company purchased 1,000 common shares of GM Holding from Toronto Stock Exchange at $92.17 per share. The equity instrument is purchased for the purpose of trading.

2) On June 30, 2016, Norman Company received a dividend from GM Holding of $2.30 per share.

3) On December 31, 2016, the trading price of GM Holding went down to $91.05 per share.

4) On January 19, 2017, Norman Company sold 500 GM Holding shares at $90.05 per share.

Record journal entries of the provided investment activities for Norman Company.

Date	Account Title and Explanation	Debit	Credit

AP-7B (❶ ❸)

On June 1, 2016, Rogers Company purchased 150,000 of Supply Company's 600,000 outstanding common shares. Rogers Company intends to gain control over decisions related to quality assurance made by Supply Company's Board of Directors.

Required

a) What level of influence does Rogers Company have over Supply Company solely based on the percentage of ownership? Which accounting method should be used for recording this investment?

_____

_____

_____

_____

b) Based on the current ownership percentage, can Rogers Company control all decisions of quality assurance made by Supply Company?

_____

_____

_____

AP-8B (❸)

On March 16, 2016, Victor Company, a public company, purchased 10% of the 1,000,000 outstanding common shares issued by Water Company at a price of $16 per share. Victor Company is planning to acquire more shares in the future to gradually gain influence over Water Company's operating decisions. Victor Company intends to maintain those common shares for at least 10 years.

During 2016, the following activities occurred in regards to this investment.

1) On June 30, 2016, Victor Company received a cash dividend from Water Company for $1.08 per share.

2) On December 31, 2016, the year-end date of Victor Company, Water's common shares were traded at $15.00 per share.

Prepare journal entries to record the acquisition of common shares, receipt of cash dividends and the year-end adjustments related to this investment in Victor Company's books.

Date	Account Title and Explanation	Debit	Credit

AP-9B (❸)

On January 31, 2016, Alberta Holding purchased 30% of the 800,000 outstanding common shares from Brain Company and paid $720,000 in cash. Alberta Holding is aiming to set up a strategic partnership with Brain Company to explore overseas markets. Alberta's year-end is on December 31. Alberta Holding follows IFRS and the following activities occurred in regards to this investment during 2016.

1) Brain Company recorded a net income of $689,000 for its year ended on October 1, 2016.

2) On December 1, 2016, Brain Company paid cash dividends of $200,000 .

Required

a) Prepare journal entries to record the acquisition of Brain Company's common shares.

b) Prepare journal entries to record revenue of investment from Brain Company on October 1, 2016.

c) Prepare journal entries to record the receipt of cash dividends on December 1, 2016.

Date	Account Title and Explanation	Debit	Credit

d) What would be the balance of the Investment on Alberta Holding's books on December 31, 2016?

_____

_____

_____

_____

Analysis

Assume by December 2016, Alberta's market analyst noticed that Brain Company's common shares are now traded at $8 per share, significantly higher than the original purchase price at the beginning of 2016. Should this change be reflected on Alberta Holding's financial statements? Give analysis on whether Alberta Holding should make adjustments at its year-end to reflect this significant change in value.

_____

_____

_____

_____

_____

_____

AP-10B (❸)

Elle Company is a private company that follows ASPE. On August 1, 2016, the company purchased 35% of Feng Company's 100,000 common shares outstanding. Elle Company paid $630,000 of cash in total for those shares. Elle Company is considered to have significant influence over Feng Company and applies the cost method for recording this investment. Elle has a year-end on December 31.

Required

a) Prepare journal entries for the acquisition of Feng Company's common shares by Elle Company.

b) Prepare journal entries for the dividends received from Feng Company on December 1, 2016. Feng Company paid $1 cash dividend per common share.

c) Prepare journal entries for adjusting the fair value of this investment by Elle Company on December 31, 2016. Each share was sold for $18.50.

d) Prepare journal entries for the sale of 50% of this investment by Elle Company on March 31, 2017. Each share was sold for $19.08.

Date	Account Title and Explanation	Debit	Credit

AP-11B (❶ ❹)

Different accounting methods of recording investments impact different accounts in either the balance sheet or income statement.

Required

a) Indicate which accounting method should be used under IFRS for recording each transaction listed in the table below. The first transaction has been completed as an example.

Item No.	Scenario	Valuation Method
1	Accrued interest of $150 for a 120-day T-bill that the investor intends to hold until maturity for interest revenue.	Amortized Cost
2	Sale of a long-term investment bond for $10,300 cash before maturity. The bond had a book value of $10,000. The purpose of this investment was for earning interest revenue.	
3	Received interest payment of $4,000 for a long-term bond investment. The interest revenue earned was $4,300.	
4	A non-strategic short-term bond investment accrued interest revenue of $200 at year-end. The purpose of this investment was for trading.	
5	The fair value of a non-strategic short-term bond decreased by $600. The purpose of this investment was for trading.	
6	The fair value of a long-term bond investment increased by $3,600. This bond is invested with the purpose of earning interest.	
7	An associate company reported $10,000 of net loss. The investor owns 25% of an associate's common shares with significant influence.	
8	A fair value of a long-term equity investment decreased by $2,000. The investor has insignificant influence.	

b) Complete the table to show how each transaction from the table above impacts each account for the investor. Assume the investor follows IFRS. The first row has been completed as an example.

| | Income Statement | | | | | | Balance Sheet | | | |
| | Revenue | | Expense | | OCI | | Current Assets | | Non-Current Assets | |
Item No.	Debit	Credit	Debit	Credit	Debit	Credit	Debit	Credit	Debit	Credit
1		150					150			
2										
3										
4										
5										
6										
7										
8										

AP-12B (❶ ❷ ❸)

George Company, a public company, adopted IFRS standards since 2011. It has a year-end of December 31. The following activities are related to its investments over the course of three years.

1) On February 2, 2016, George Company acquired 5% of the 1,000,000 outstanding common shares of Helen Company, for the purpose of short-term trading, at $17.45 per share.

2) On December 31, 2016, George Company received a cash dividend from Helen Company for a total of $64,000.

3) On December 31, 2016, Helen Company's common shares were traded for $16.55 per share on the local stock exchange.

4) On March 16, 2017, George Company purchased 150,000 of 1,000,000 outstanding common shares of Siya Company for a market price of $10.00 per share. The purpose of this investment was to create a business alliance agreement with Siya Company.

5) On December 31, 2017, George Company received a cash dividend payment of $1.28 per share from Helen Company and $1 per share from Siya Company.

6) The shares of Helen Company and Siya Company were trading at $17.50 and $11.00 per share respectively on December 31, 2017.

7) On January 31, 2018, George Company sold the investment in Helen Company for $900,000 cash.

Required

a) Discuss which accounting method should be used by George Company for each type of investment.

_____

_____

_____

_____

b) Prepare journal entries to record all of George Company's activities.

Date	Account Title and Explanation	Debit	Credit

c) Calculate the balance of each investment of George Company at the end of 2016 and 2017.

_____

_____

_____

_____

_____

_____

Analysis

Assume in 2018, George Company purchased an additional 100,000 shares from a total of 1,000,0000 outstanding common shares of Siya company. Would this transaction have any impacts on this investment? Explain.

_____

_____

_____

_____

_____

AP-13B (❶ ❸)

The following are investment activities for Quentin Company. Assume the company follows IFRS and has a year-end of December 31.

1) On January 1, 2016, Quentin Company spent $19,750 to purchase a $20,000, 90-day T-bill at 5% interest. Quentin Company is planning to hold the investment until maturity.

2) On March 1, 2016, Quentin Company made a strategic business investment of $90,000 in Hallow Company, by acquiring 25% of its 100,000 outstanding shares.

3) On July 30, 2016, Quentin Company received a cash dividend from Hallow Company of $0.18 per share. A total profit of $65,000 was reported on Hallow Company's Income Statement published on July 1, 2016.

4) On December 31, 2016, Quentin Company's accountant notices that Hallow Company's shares were trading at $4.00 per share.

Prepare journal entries to record the above investment activities.

Date	Account Title and Explanation	Debit	Credit

Analysis

When Quentin Company's accountant noticed the trading price change of Hallow Company on December 31, 2016, the CEO of Quentin Company suggested to make a year-end fair value adjustment to "reflect the true market value of the investment." As the Hallow Company's accountant, explain if fair value adjustment is needed. Prepare journal entries if necessary.

_____

_____

_____

_____

_____

AP-14B (❸)

Mill Inc. acquired 30% of the 800,000 outstanding common shares from Nixy Company and paid $3,300,000 in cash on January 1, 2016. On July 1, 2016, Nixy Company reported a profit of $900,000 on its annual financial statements, ending June 30, 2016. Nixy paid cash dividends of $0.25 per share, on July 30, 2016. Mill Company uses ASPE standards and decided to use the cost method to account for this investment from the beginning. If the equity method was used instead, how much would it affect the ending balance of the investment account at its year-end of December 31, 2016?

_____

_____

_____

_____

_____

_____

AP-15B (❸)

Shaw Company had the following activities in relation to its investments in 2016. The company follows IFRS with June 30 as its year-end.

1) On January 1, 2016, Shaw Company purchased 35,000 (or 35%) common shares from Tang Company for $859,950.

2) On March 31, 2016, Shaw Company's accountant received financial statements from Tang Company, which reported a net loss of $560,000 for the year ending February 28, 2016.

3) On April 30, 2016, Shaw Company received cash dividends from Tang Company of $0.05 per share.

4) On June 30, 2016, Tang Company's shares were traded at $25.25 per share.

Required

a) Prepare journal entries to record the above activities assuming significant influence is achieved.

Date	Account Title and Explanation	Debit	Credit

b) Prepare journal entries to record the above activities assuming significant influence is **not** achieved.

Date	Account Title and Explanation	Debit	Credit

Analysis

Assume Shaw Company adopts ASPE standards, how would that affect the journal entries when applying fair value method?

_____

_____

_____

_____

_____

_____

_____

_____

_____

Case Study

CS-1 (❷)

A five-year bond of $500,000 was issued on March 1, 2016 with the coupon rate of 6%. The market interest rate was 4% at that time. Interests are paid semi-annually on March 1 and September 1 every year. Both the issuer and the investor have a year-end date on December 31. Assume both the investor and issuer follow IFRS.

Required

a) Using the Present Value Factors, prepare an amortization table from the issuance date to maturity.

Interest Period	A Interest Payment	B Interest Expense/Revenue	C Premium Amortization	D Bond Amortized Cost

b) Assume the issuer's accountant is using the effective interest method. Prepare the journal entries from the bond issuer's perspective for the issue date of the bonds, first interest payment, first year-end adjustment and retirement of bonds on March 1, 2021. (Note: Do not record the last interest payment on March 1, 2021.)

Date	Account Title and Explanation	Debit	Credit

c) Assume the investor's accountant is using the amortized cost method. Prepare the journal entries from the investor's perspective for the issue date of the bonds, first interest receipt, first year-end adjustment and cash receipt of principal at maturity on March 1, 2021. (Note: Do not record the last interest receipt on March 1, 2021.)

Date	Account Title and Explanation	Debit	Credit

d) When amortizing the discount or premium on bonds, what is the main difference(s) between the issuer's and the investor's recording?

_____

_____

_____

_____

_____

_____

_____

e) Under IFRS, if the debt investment is for the purpose of making short-term profits instead of being held until maturity, investors are allowed to use fair value through profit and loss method. Although investment classification is strictly based on management's intention at the purchase date, what are some of the reasons that an investor may generally prefer the fair value through profit and loss method over the amortized cost method?

_____

_____

_____

_____

_____

_____

_____

_____

_____

_____

_____

_____

_____

Chapter 10

THE STATEMENT OF CASH FLOW

LEARNING OUTCOMES

❶ Classify operating, investing and financing activities

❷ Prepare a cash flow statement using the indirect method

❸ Calculate book value and cash received for selling non-current assets

❹ Explain the concept of free cash flow and its importance for potential investors

❺ Discuss ethics and control issues related to cash flow

Appendix

❻ Prepare a cash flow statement using the direct method

AMEENGAGE *Access **ameengage.com** for integrated resources including tutorials, practice exercises, the digital textbook and more.*

Assessment Questions

AS-1 (❶)

Is the cash flow statement an optional statement? Explain.

_____

_____

_____

_____

_____

AS-2 (❶)

Identify the three ways a business can generate and use cash.

_____

_____

_____

_____

_____

AS-3 (❶)

What does cash flow from operating activities represent?

_____

_____

_____

AS-4 (❶)

What does cash flow from investing activities represent?

_____

_____

_____

AS-5 (❶)

What does cash flow from financing activities represent?

_____

_____

_____

_____

AS-6 (❷)

Which financial statements are required to prepare a cash flow statement?

_____

_____

_____

AS-7 (❷)

Which items appear in the cash flow from operating activities section of the cash flow statement using the indirect method?

_____

_____

_____

_____

AS-8 (❷)

Which items appear in the cash flow from investing activities section of the cash flow statement?

_____

_____

_____

AS-9 (❷)

Which items appear in the cash flow from financing activities section of the cash flow statement?

_____

_____

_____

AS-10 (❸)

What does a gain on the sale of equipment indicate?

_____

_____

AS-11 (❷)

How is a gain on the sale of equipment shown on the cash flow statement using the indirect method?

_____

_____

_____

_____

AS-12 (❹)

Define free cash flow.

_____

_____

AS-13 (❹)

Why would an investor or creditor want to see a company show a positive free cash flow amount?

_____

_____

_____

AS-14 (❺)

What are some actions a company may be tempted to take to unethically and artificially improve its cash flow statement presentation?

_____

_____

_____

_____

AS-15 (❻)

What is the difference in the presentation of the cash flow statement between the indirect and the direct methods?

_____

_____

_____

_____

_____

AS-16 (❻)

Using the direct method, how can we calculate the amount of cash spent on inventory?

_____

_____

_____

_____

Application Questions Group A

AP-1A (❶)

For each item listed, indicate how the item will impact cash flow (increase, decrease or no change) using the indirect method.

Item	Effect on Cash
Net Income	
Increase in Accounts Payable	
Decrease in Accounts Receivable	
Purchase of Property, Plant and Equipment	
Payment of Bank Loan	
Increase in Inventory	
Pay Dividends	
Increase in Loans	
Increase in Prepaid Insurance	

AP-2A (❶)

Indicate the section of the cash flow statement where each item would be located (operating, investing or financing activities) using the indirect method.

Item	Section
Change in Accounts Payable	
Change in Inventory	
Change in Property, Plant and Equipment	
Change in Non-Current Portion of Bank Loan	
Change in Current Portion of Bank Loan	
Change in Prepaid Rent	
Change in Accounts Receivable	
Change in Common Shares	
Gain on Sale of Property, Plant and Equipment	

AP-3A (❷)

The net income for the year ended on December 31, 2016 for RC Corporation was $120,000.
Additional data for the year is provided below.

Purchase of property, plant and equipment	$280,000
Depreciation of property, plant and equipment	14,000
Dividends declared	50,000
Decrease in accounts receivable	29,000
Loss on sale of equipment	13,000

Calculate the change in cash from operating activities using the indirect method.

_____

_____

_____

_____

_____

AP-4A (❷)

Ashe Inc. reported the following data for 2016.

Income Statement	
Net Income	$30,000
Depreciation Expense	4,000
Balance Sheet	
Increase in Accounts Receivable	9,000
Decrease in Accounts Payable	7,000

Calculate the increase (decrease) in cash from operating activities.

_____

_____

_____

_____

_____

_____

AP-5A (❷)

The net income for the year ended on August 31, 2016 for Wonderstruck Corporation was $147,000. Additional data for the year is provided below.

Purchase of property, plant and equipment	$257,000
Depreciation of equipment	$11,000
Dividends paid	$42,000
Net increase in accounts receivable	$22,000
Loss on sale of property	$17,000

Calculate the increase or decrease in cash from operating activities.

_____

_____

_____

_____

_____

_____

_____

AP-6A (❷)

Mellon Incorporated had a net income for 2016 of $320,000. Included on the income statement was a loss on sale of equipment for $5,000, a gain on the sale of investments for $15,000, depreciation of $8,000 and interest of $3,000. Calculate the increase or decrease in cash from operating activities using the indirect method.

_____

_____

_____

_____

_____

_____

_____

Analysis

Does net income, after being adjusted by the non-cash items on the income statement, represent the actual amount of cash received through operating activities by the company during the year?

_____

_____

_____

AP-7A (❷)

The following information pertains to Tree Company for the fiscal year 2016.

Purchase of plant and equipment	$35,000
Purchase of long-term investments	$19,000
Increase in accounts receivable	$7,100
Repayment of bonds payable	$12,000
Depreciation of plant and equipment	$10,000

Calculate the increase or decrease in cash from investing activities.

_____

_____

_____

AP-8A (❷)

The Marking Company's cash account decreased by $20,000. Cash increase from operating activities was $17,000. Net cash decrease from investing activities was $22,000. Calculate the cash increase (or decrease) from financing activities.

_____

_____

_____

_____

_____

_____

AP-9A (❷)

The Grading Company's cash account decreased by $14,000. Cash increase from operating activities was $21,000. Net cash decrease from investing activities was $22,000. Based on this information, calculate the cash increase (or decrease) from financing activities.

_____

_____

_____

_____

_____

_____

AP-10A (❸)

Allen Woods has just started working as an accountant for Stickla Supplies. Unfortunately, the company had no proper accounting system in place and Allen had to start everything from scratch. He has been provided with some items from the company's balance sheet and income statement for the end of 2016.

Going through the company's purchase receipts and some other financial documents, Allen realized that Stickla purchased $2,500 of equipment in 2016 and the balance of property, plant and equipment and accumulated depreciation at the end of 2015 was $11,000 and $2,900 respectively. Accounts payable balance was not affected by any investment activities during 2016.

Accounts	2016
Property, Plant and Equipment	$10,000
Accumulated Depreciation	$3,600
Accounts Payable	$4,000
Current Portion of Bank Loan	$15,000
Retained Earnings	$5,400
Depreciation Expense	$1,200
Loss on Sale of Equipment	$300

Based on the information provided, help Allen fill the missing information in the table below.

Which section of the Cash Flow Statement is affected?	
How much PPE was sold in 2016?	
What was the accumulated depreciation for the PPE sold?	
What was the book value of the PPE sold?	
How much cash was received from the sale?	
How much cash was paid out for the purchase?	
What was the net change in cash resulting from PPE?	

AP-11A (❷)

Balance sheet accounts for Planet Inc. contain the following amounts at the end of 2015 and 2016.

Planet Inc. Balance Sheet As at December 31		
	2016	**2015**
Assets		
Current Assets		
Cash	$7,500	$5,000
Accounts Receivable	21,000	15,000
Prepaid Expenses	2,500	2,000
Inventory	37,000	28,000
Total Current Assets	68,000	50,000
Long-Term Assets		
Equipment	196,000	175,000
Less: Accumulated Depreciation	(41,000)	(32,000)
Total Long-Term Assets	155,000	143,000
Total Assets	$223,000	$193,000
Liabilities		
Current Liabilities	$33,000	$33,000
Non-Current Liabilities	30,000	35,000
Total Liabilities	63,000	68,000
Shareholders' Equity		
Common Shares	75,000	60,000
Retained Earnings	85,000	65,000
Total Shareholders' Equity	160,000	125,000
Total Liabilities and Equity	$223,000	$193,000

Assume current liabilities include only items from operations (e.g. accounts payable, taxes payable). Non-current liabilities include items from financing (e.g. bonds and other non-current liabilities).

Note that there was no sale of equipment throughout the year.

Prepare the cash flow statement for 2016 using the indirect method. Assume no dividends were declared or paid in 2016.

AP-12A (❷ ❻)

Breakwater Boats sells boating accessories. At the end of 2016, the income statement and comparative balance sheet were prepared as shown below.

	Breakwater Boats Balance Sheet As at December 31	
	2016	**2015**
Assets		
Current Assets		
Cash	$73,870	$62,500
Accounts Receivable	94,800	87,500
Inventory	327,000	245,700
Prepaid Expenses	14,500	14,500
Total Current Assets	510,170	410,200
Non-Current Assets		
Property, Plant and Equipment[1]		
Land	0	44,000
Equipment	340,000	340,000
Less: Accumulated Depreciation	(26,200)	(24,500)
Total Non-Current Assets	313,800	359,500
Total Assets	$823,970	$769,700
Liabilities and Equity		
Liabilities		
Current Liabilities		
Accounts Payable	$52,600	$45,700
Current Portion of Bank Loan	8,500	8,500
Total Current Liabilities	61,100	54,200
Non-Current Portion of Bank Loan	50,100	58,600
Total Liabilities	111,200	112,800
Shareholders' Equity		
Common Shares	150,000	150,000
Retained Earnings	562,770	506,900
Total Shareholders' Equity	712,770	656,900
Total Liabilities and Equity	$823,970	$769,700

[1] Property, Plant & Equipment

During 2016, land was sold for a gain of $6,000. There was no purchase of equipment throughout the year.

Breakwater Boats
Income Statement
For the Year Ended December 31, 2016

Sales	$562,000
Cost of Goods Sold	365,300
Gross Profit	196,700
Operating Expenses	
Depreciation Expense	1,700
Other Operating Expenses	61,200
Total Operating Expenses	62,900
Operating Income	133,800
Other Revenue	
Gain on Sale of Land	6,000
Operating Income before Tax	139,800
Income Tax Expense	48,930
Net Income	$90,870

Required

a)   Create the cash flow statement using the indirect method.

b) Create the cash flow statement using the direct method. Assume accounts payable is only for the purchase of inventory.

Analysis

Explain the main activities that caused Breakwater Boats' net cash flow to increase or decrease.

AP-13A (❷ ❸ ❻)

The balance sheet and income statement for Zooyo Appliance are presented below.

Zooyo Appliance Balance Sheet As at December 31		
	2016	**2015**
Assets		
Cash	$37,580	$15,000
Accounts Receivable	17,000	16,000
Inventory	21,000	27,000
Total Current Assets	75,580	58,000
Property, Plant & Equipment		
Land	110,000	80,000
Equipment	130,000	160,000
Less: Accumulated Depreciation	(26,500)	(30,000)
Total Assets	$289,080	$268,000
Liabilities		
Accounts Payable	$29,000	$35,000
Current Portion of Bank Loan	18,000	18,000
Current Liabilities	47,000	53,000
Non-Current Portion of Bank Loan	80,000	65,000
Total Liabilities	127,000	118,000
Shareholders' Equity		
Common Shares	75,000	70,000
Retained Earnings	87,080	80,000
Shareholders' Equity	162,080	150,000
Liabilities and Shareholders' Equity	$289,080	$268,000

Zooyo Appliance Income Statement For the Year Ended December 31, 2016	
Sales	$142,000
Cost of Goods Sold	92,000
Gross Profit	50,000
Expenses	
Depreciation Expense	4,500
Other Operating Expenses	17,900
Total Expenses	22,400
Operating Income	27,600
Other Expenses	
Loss on Sale of Equipment	(3,200)
Operating Income before Tax	24,400
Income Tax Expense	7,320
Net Income (Loss)	$17,080

Notes: There was no sale of land or purchase of equipment during the year. The company declared and paid dividends during the year.

Required

a) Prepare the cash flow statement for December 31, 2016 using the indirect method.

b) Create the cash flow statement using the direct method. Assume accounts payable is only
   for the purchase of inventory.

AP-14A (❷ ❸ ❻)

The balance sheet and income statement for Demgo Inc. are presented below.

Demgo Inc. Balance Sheet As at December 31		
	2016	**2015**
Assets		
Cash	$20,140	$21,000
Accounts Receivable	17,000	19,000
Inventory	21,000	15,000
Total Current Assets	58,140	55,000
Property, Plant & Equipment		
Land	110,000	60,000
Machinery	100,000	140,000
Less: Accumulated Depreciation	(40,500)	(60,000)
Total Assets	$227,640	$195,000
Liabilities		
Accounts Payable	$29,000	$25,000
Current Portion of Bank Loan	22,000	22,000
Current Liabilities	51,000	47,000
Non-Current Portion of Bank Loan	70,000	65,000
Total Liabilities	121,000	112,000
Shareholders' Equity		
Common Shares	85,000	70,000
Retained Earnings	21,640	13,000
Shareholders' Equity	106,640	83,000
Liabilities and Shareholders' Equity	$227,640	$195,000

Demgo Inc. Income Statement For the Year Ended December 31, 2016	
Sales	$130,000
Cost of Goods Sold	72,000
Gross Profit	58,000
Expenses	
Depreciation Expense	20,500
Other Operating Expenses	14,000
Total Expenses	34,500
Operating Income	23,500
Other Revenue	
Gain on Sale of Machinery	1,700
Operating Income before Tax	25,200
Income Tax Expense	7,560
Net Income (Loss)	$17,640

Notes: There was no sale of land.

Machinery was purchased for an amount of $80,000.

The company declared and paid dividends during the year.

Required

a) Prepare the cash flow statement for December 31, 2016 using the indirect method.

b) Create the cash flow statement using the direct method. Assume accounts payable is only for the purchase of inventory.

AP-15A (❷ ❸ ❻)

The balance sheet and income statement for Vispara Company are presented below.

Vispara Company Balance Sheet As at December 31		
	2016	2015
Assets		
Cash	$133,400	$75,000
Accounts Receivable	47,000	26,000
Inventory	72,000	42,000
Total Current Assets	252,400	143,000
Property, Plant & Equipment		
Land	90,000	100,000
Equipment	90,000	130,000
Less: Accumulated Depreciation	(45,000)	(60,000)
Total Assets	$387,400	$313,000
Liabilities		
Accounts Payable	$35,000	$65,000
Current Portion of Bank Loan	40,000	40,000
Current Liabilities	75,000	105,000
Non-Current Portion of Bank Loan	140,000	95,000
Total Liabilities	215,000	200,000
Shareholders' Equity		
Common Shares	85,000	75,000
Retained Earnings	87,400	38,000
Shareholders' Equity	172,400	113,000
Liabilities and Shareholders' Equity	$387,400	$313,000

Vispara Company Income Statement For the Year Ended December 31, 2016	
Sales	$380,000
Cost of Goods Sold	247,000
Gross Profit	133,000
Expenses	
Depreciation Expense	5,000
Other Operating Expenses	29,600
Total Expenses	34,600
Operating Income	98,400
Other Revenue (Expenses)	
Loss on Sale of Equipment	(5,400)
Gain on Sale of Land	5,000
Operating Income before Tax	98,000
Income Tax Expense	29,400
Net Income (Loss)	$68,600

Notes

The company paid cash dividends during 2016.

The company did not make a bank loan payment during 2016.

The company did not purchase any equipment during 2016.

The company did not purchase any land during 2016.

Required

a)   Prepare the cash flow statement for December 31, 2016 using the indirect method.

b) Create the cash flow statement using the direct method. Assume accounts payable is only for the purchase of inventory.

Analysis

a) Are there any concerns based on the cash flow statement?

_____

_____

_____

_____

b) Are there any concerns in the cash flow from operating activities section?

_____

_____

_____

_____

AP-16A (❷)

2016 has been a great year for Exany Company, which managed to earn $56,000 of net income. Therefore, the board decided to declare and pay dividends by year-end.

Based on the following information, answer the following questions.

Accounts	2016	2015
Retained Earnings	$91,000	$67,000
Common Shares	$120,000	$110,000

a) How much dividends were paid in 2016?	
b) Which section of the cash flow statement is affected?	
c) Assuming only the information given impacted the section of the cash flow statement indicated in b), what is the net change in cash for this section?	

AP-17A (❶ ❹)

Cleancarpet Vacuums sells vacuum accessories. At the end of 2016, the cash flow statement below was prepared.

Cleancarpet Vacuums Cash Flow Statement For the Year Ended December 31, 2016		
Cash Flow from Operating Activities		
Net Income	$83,800	
Add: Depreciation Expense	4,760	
Deduct: Gain on Sale of Equipment	(7,200)	
Change in Current Assets and Current Liabilities		
Decrease in Accounts Receivable	2,210	
Increase in Inventory	(46,800)	
Increase in Accounts Payable	6,000	
Change in Cash due to Operating Activities		$42,770
Cash Flow from Investing Activities		
Sale of Equipment	20,300	
Change in Cash due to Investing Activities		20,300
Cash Flow from Financing Activities		
Payment of Bank Loan	(19,100)	
Payment of Cash Dividend	(23,700)	
Change in Cash due to Financing Activities		(42,800)
Net Increase (Decrease) in Cash		20,270
Cash at the Beginning of the Year		68,300
Cash at the End of the Year		$88,570

Required

a) How much of the company's cash is from day-to-day operations?

b) Why does the company have positive cash flow from investing activities? Would such positive cash flow from investing activities be sustainable?

_____

_____

_____

_____

_____

_____

_____

c) Calculate Cleancarpet Vacuums' free cash flow in 2016.

_____

_____

_____

Analysis

What could Cleancarpet Vacuums do if selling the equipment were not an action the company could take, yet it still wanted to have a positive net cash flow at the end of the year?

_____

_____

_____

_____

_____

_____

_____

_____

Application Questions Group B

AP-1B (❶)

Indicate which section each item in the table below would appear in a cash flow statement using the indirect method. Also indicate whether the item would increase or decrease cash using the indirect method.

Item	Section	Effect on Cash
Loss on sale of equipment		
Decrease in accounts payable		
Increase in inventory		
Depreciation expense		
Gain on sale of investments		
Dividends paid		
Issued shares in the company		
Net income		
Decrease in bank loan		
Sold equipment		
Decrease accounts receivable		

AP-2B (❷)

Bonus Company had the following amounts in its cash flow statement for the year ended December 31, 2016.

Net decrease in cash from operating activities	$100,000
Net decrease in cash from investing activities	400,000
Net increase in cash from financing activities	350,000
Cash balance, January 1, 2016	600,000

Calculate the cash balance at December 31, 2016.

AP-3B (❷)

The net income for the year ended December 31, 2016 for Kersley Company was $73,000.
Additional information is shown below.

Interest expense on borrowing	$8,000
Increase in accounts receivable	10,000
Decrease in prepaid expense	3,000
Decrease in accounts payable	4,000
Dividends paid to common shareholders	14,000

Calculate the increase (decrease) in cash from operating activities.

_____

_____

_____

_____

_____

AP-4B (❷)

Use the following information to prepare the operating activities section of a cash flow
statement for MNO Co. for 2016 using the indirect method.

Net income	$140,000
Increase in inventory	30,000
Increase in accounts payable	20,000
Depreciation expense	55,000
Increase in accounts receivable	18,000
Gain on sale of land	25,000

_____

_____

_____

_____

_____

_____

_____

AP-5B (❷)

Danes Company had net income for 2016 of $120,000. Included in net income was a depreciation of $3,000, a gain of the sale of land of $5,000 and income taxes of $30,000. Using the information given, calculate the increase or decrease in cash from operating activities using the indirect method.

_____

_____

_____

_____

Analysis

Why are some items from the income statement added back to net income on the cash flow statement?

_____

_____

_____

_____

AP-6B (❷)

The following information pertains to Bush Company for the fiscal year 2016.

Purchase of plant and equipment	$33,000
Sale of long-term investments	12,000
Increase in accounts payable	6,000
Repayment of bonds payable	15,000
Depreciation of plant and equipment	7,000

Calculate the increase (decrease) in cash from investing activities.

_____

_____

_____

AP-7B (❷)

The following events took place during 2016 at Bernard Company. Based on the information given, calculate how much cash inflow or outflow there was from investing activities.

Gain on sale of investments	$4,000
Sale of investments (including gain)	$50,000
Issued company shares	$60,000
Paid off a bank loan	$30,000
Purchased equipment	$70,000

_____

_____

_____

_____

AP-8B (❷)

The following events took place during 2016 to Shaw Company. Based on the information given, calculate how much cash inflow or outflow there was from financing activities.

Loss on sale of land	$10,000
Sale of land (including loss)	$110,000
Issued company shares	$120,000
Paid off a bank loan	$50,000
Paid dividends	$30,000
Depreciation Expense	$6,000

_____

_____

_____

_____

_____

Analysis

If Shaw Company's net income during 2016 was $25,000, identify a potential concern from the cash flows from financing activities section.

_____

_____

_____

AP-9B (❷)

The following events took place during 2016 to Robinson Company. Based on the information given, calculate how much cash inflow or outflow there was from investing activities and financing activities.

Gain on sale of equipment	$2,000
Sale of equipment (including gain)	$90,000
Purchase of long-term investments	$65,000
Issued company shares	$60,000
Received a bank loan	$40,000
Paid dividends	$20,000
Increase in inventory	$24,000

_____

_____

_____

_____

_____

_____

_____

_____

Analysis

Suppose Robinson Company had a net increase in cash of $50,000. Explain why the company may be in trouble despite having a large increase in cash during the year.

_____

_____

_____

_____

_____

_____

_____

AP-10B (❸)

Factsy Inc. is planning to make the best use out of its cash on hand by purchasing some additional long-term investments. Factsy's long-term investments are held at cost. In January 2016, Factsy bought additional investments. The company also sold part of its investments in November 2016 due to a sudden growth in the value of its holdings. December 31 is its year-end.

Below are the data of Factsy Company.

Accounts	2016	2015
Long-Term Investment	$120,000	$110,000
Purchase of Investment	$40,000	
Gain on Sale of Investment	$5,000	

Calculate the net change in cash resulting from the long-term investment.

_____

_____

_____

_____

Analysis

Factsy's bookkeeper believes that the net change in cash from the investing activities must be a positive number (a cash inflow) as a result of a big gain on the sale of investment. Do you agree with this comment? Explain.

AP-11B (❷)

Flax Corporation's balance sheet accounts as of December 31, 2016 and 2015 are presented below.

Flax Corp. Balance Sheet As at December 31	2016	2015
Assets		
Current Assets		
Cash	$460,000	$300,000
Short-Term Investments	600,000	-
Accounts Receivable	1,020,000	1,020,000
Inventory	1,360,000	1,200,000
Total Current Assets	3,440,000	2,520,000
Long-Term Assets		
Long-Term Investments	400,000	800,000
Equipment	3,100,000	2,500,000
Less: Accumulated Depreciation	(900,000)	(600,000)
Total Long-Term Assets	2,600,000	2,700,000
Total Assets	$6,040,000	$5,220,000
Liabilities		
Current Liabilities	$2,300,000	$2,000,000
Non-Current Liabilities	800,000	700,000
Total Liabilities	3,100,000	2,700,000
Shareholders' Equity		
Common Shares	1,800,000	1,680,000
Retained Earnings	1,140,000	840,000
Total Shareholders' Equity	2,940,000	2,520,000
Total Liabilities and Equity	$6,040,000	$5,220,000

Assume current liabilities include only items from operations (e.g. accounts payable, taxes payable). Non-current liabilities include items from financing (e.g. bonds and other non-current liabilities).

Note that there was no sale of equipment throughout the year.

Prepare the cash flow statement for 2016 using the indirect method. Assume the net income for 2016 was $300,000.

AP-12B (❷ ❻)

Vortex Manufacturing makes and sells integrated circuit boards. At the end of 2016, the income statement and comparative balance sheet were prepared as shown below.

Vortex Manufacturing Balance Sheet As at December 31		
	2016	**2015**
Assets		
Current Assets		
Cash	$239,820	$135,640
Accounts Receivable	242,100	265,300
Inventory	503,200	465,300
Prepaid Expenses	26,500	26,500
Total Current Assets	1,011,620	892,740
Non-Current Assets		
Property, Plant and Equipment[1]		
Land	0	16,000
Equipment	840,400	840,400
Less: Accumulated Depreciation	(102,300)	(95,600)
Total Non-Current Assets	738,100	760,800
Total Assets	$1,749,720	$1,653,540
Liabilities and Equity		
Liabilities		
Current Liabilities		
Accounts Payable	$305,600	$324,500
Current Portion of Bank Loan	32,000	23,000
Total Current Liabilities	337,600	347,500
Non-Current Portion of Bank Loan	205,000	185,000
Total Liabilities	542,600	532,500
Shareholders' Equity		
Common Shares	290,000	260,000
Retained Earnings	917,120	861,040
Total Shareholders' Equity	1,207,120	1,121,040
Total Liabilities and Equity	$1,749,720	$1,653,540

[1]   Property, Plant & Equipment

During 2016, land was sold for a loss of $5,000. There was no purchase of equipment throughout the year.

The company did not pay off any amount of the bank loan.

Vortex Manufacturing **Income Statement** **For the Year Ended December 31, 2016**	
Sales	$2,650,000
Cost of Goods Sold	1,722,500
Gross Profit	927,500
Operating Expenses	
Depreciation Expense	6,700
Other Operating Expenses	752,600
Total Operating Expenses	759,300
Operating Income	168,200
Other Expenses	
Loss on Sale of Land	(5,000)
Operating Income before Tax	163,200
Income Tax	57,120
Net Income	$106,080

Required

a) Create the cash flow statement using the indirect method.

b) Create the cash flow statement using the direct method. Assume accounts payable is only
    for the purchase of inventory.

AP-13B (❷ ❸ ❻)

The balance sheet and income statement for Venus Company are presented below.

Venus Company Balance Sheet As at December 31		
	2016	**2015**
Assets		
Cash	$191,410	$94,000
Accounts Receivable	30,000	34,000
Inventory	42,000	50,000
Total Current Assets	263,410	178,000
Property, Plant and Equipment		
Land	90,000	100,000
Building	125,000	130,000
Less: Accumulated Depreciation	(62,000)	(60,000)
Total Assets	$416,410	$348,000
Liabilities		
Accounts Payable	$76,000	$65,000
Current Portion of Bank Loan	45,000	40,000
Current Liabilities	121,000	105,000
Non-Current Portion of Bank Loan	120,000	95,000
Total Liabilities	241,000	200,000
Shareholders' Equity		
Common Shares	85,000	75,000
Retained Earnings	90,410	73,000
Shareholders' Equity	175,410	148,000
Liabilities and Shareholders' Equity	$416,410	$348,000

Venus Company Income Statement For the Year Ended December 31, 2016	
Sales	$380,000
Cost of Goods Sold	255,000
Gross Profit	125,000
Expenses	
Depreciation Expense	42,000
Other Operating Expense	28,500
Total Expenses	70,500
Operating Income	54,500
Other Revenue (Expenses)	
Loss on Sale of Building	(5,400)
Gain on Sale of Land	3,200
Operating Income before Tax	52,300
Income Tax Expense	15,690
Net Income (Loss)	$36,610

Notes: Building and land were purchased for amounts of $115,000, and $200,000 respectively.

The company declared and paid dividends during the year.

The company did not pay off any amount of the bank loan.

Required

a) Prepare the cash flow statement for December 31, 2016 using the indirect method.

b) Create the cash flow statement using the direct method. Assume accounts payable is only for the purchase of inventory.

AP-14B (❷ ❸ ❻)

The balance sheet and income statement for Twely Inc. are presented below.

Twely Inc. Balance Sheet As at December 31		
	2016	**2015**
Assets		
Cash	$62,927	$56,000
Accounts Receivable	27,000	23,000
Inventory	24,500	18,000
Total Current Assets	114,427	97,000
Property, Plant and Equipment		
Long-Term Investment	42,000	45,000
Land	119,000	100,000
Equipment	89,000	76,000
Less: Accumulated Depreciation	(28,200)	(24,000)
Total Assets	$336,227	$294,000
Liabilities		
Accounts Payable	$29,000	$25,000
Current Portion of Bank Loan	22,000	22,000
Total Current Liabilities	51,000	47,000
Non-Current Portion of Bank Loan	79,000	65,000
Total Liabilities	130,000	112,000
Shareholders' Equity		
Common Shares	85,000	85,000
Retained Earnings	121,227	97,000
Shareholders' Equity	206,227	182,000
Liabilitles and Shareholders' Equity	$336,227	$294,000

Twely Inc. Income Statement For the Year Ended December 31, 2016	
Sales	$140,000
Cost of Goods Sale	76,000
Gross Profit	64,000
Expenses	
Depreciation Expense	8,200
Other Operating Expenses	14,790
Total Expenses	22,990
Operating Income	41,010
Other Revenue	
Gain on Sale of Investment	1,100
Gain on Sale of Equipment	2,500
Operating Income before Tax	44,610
Income Tax Expense	13,383
Net Income (Loss)	$31,227

Notes: There was no sale of land.

Equipment and long-term investment were purchased for amounts of $30,000 and $10,500 respectively.

The long-term investment is held at cost.

The company declared and paid dividends during the year.

The company did not pay off any amount of the bank loan.

Required

a)   Prepare the cash flow statement for December 31, 2016 using the indirect method.

b) Create the cash flow statement using the direct method. Assume accounts payable is only
    for the purchase of inventory.

AP-15B (❷ ❸ ❻)

The balance sheet and income statement for Joe's Fish Hut are presented below.

Joe's Fish Hut Balance Sheet As at December 31, 2016		
	2016	**2015**
Assets		
Cash	$2,100	$23,000
Accounts Receivable	21,000	12,000
Inventory	21,000	25,000
Total Current Assets	44,100	60,000
Property, Plant and Equipment		
Land	100,000	100,000
Equipment	170,000	150,000
Less: Accumulated Depreciation	(28,600)	(25,000)
Total Assets	$285,500	$285,000
Liabilities		
Accounts Payable	$23,000	$33,000
Current Portion of Bank Loan	12,000	12,000
Current Liabilities	35,000	45,000
Non-Current Portion of Bank Loan	48,000	60,000
Total Liabilities	83,000	105,000
Shareholders' Equity		
Common Shares	20,000	15,000
Retained Earnings	182,500	165,000
Shareholders' Equity	202,500	202,500
Liabilities and Shareholders' Equity	$285,500	$285,000

Joe's Fish Hut Income Statement For the Year Ended December 31, 2016	
Sales	$161,000
Cost of Goods Sold	112,700
Gross Profit	48,300
Operating Expenses	
Depreciation Expense	3,600
Other Operating Expense	19,700
Total Operating Expenses	23,300
Operating Income before Tax	25,000
Income Tax Expense	7,500
Net Income (Loss)	$17,500

Note

The company did not sell any equipment during the year. The company did not receive any extra amount of the bank loan in 2016.

Required

a) Prepare the cash flow statement for December 31, 2016 using the indirect method.

b) Create the cash flow statement using the direct method. Assume accounts payable is only for the purchase of inventory.

Analysis

a) Are there any concerns based on the cash flow statement?

_____

_____

_____

_____

_____

_____

_____

_____

b) Are there any concerns in the cash flow from the operating activities section?

_____

_____

_____

_____

_____

_____

_____

_____

_____

_____

_____

_____

_____

AP-16B (❶ ❷)

Carlin Corporation has prepared the following cash flow statement for the year-end.

Carlin Corporation Cash Flow Statement For the Year Ended December 31, 2016		
Cash Flow from Operating Activities		
Net Income	$56,200	
Add: Depreciation Expense	3,100	
Changes in Assets and Liabilities		
Increase in Accounts Receivable	(31,000)	
Increase in Inventory	(33,000)	
Decrease in Accounts Payable	(26,000)	
Change in Cash due to Operating Activities		($30,700)
Cash Flow from Investing Activities		
Purchase of Equipment	(95,000)	
Sale of Land	120,000	
Change in Cash due to Investing Activities		25,000
Cash Flow from Financing Activities		
Proceeds from Issuance of Common Shares	10,000	
Received Bank Loan	45,000	
Dividends Paid	(40,000)	
Change in Cash due to Financing Activities		15,000
Total Change in Cash		9,300
Opening Cash Balance		12,000
Cash at the End of the Year		$21,300

Required

a) The company had a net income during the year; however, they had a negative cash flow from operations. Identify the problems that led to a negative cash flow from operations.

_____

_____

_____

_____

b) Even though cash flow from operations was negative, total cash increased by $9,300. How did cash increase?

_____

_____

_____

c) Are there any other concerns regarding the cash flow statement that have not been covered in parts a) and b)?

_____

_____

_____

AP-17B (❶ ❷)

Dawson Corporation has prepared the following cash flow statement for the year-end.

Dawson Corporation Cash Flow Statement For the Year Ended December 31, 2016		
Cash Flow from Operating Activities		
Add: Net Income	$68,000	
Add: Depreciation Expense	3,700	
Less: Gain on Sale of Equipment	(8,000)	
Changes in Assets and Liabilities		
Decrease in Accounts Receivable	15,000	
Increase in Inventory	(60,000)	
Decrease in Accounts Payable	(5,000)	
Change in Cash due to Operating Activities		$13,700
Cash Flow from Investing Activities		
Sale of Equipment	84,000	
Purchase of Land	(240,000)	
Change in Cash due to Investing Activities		(156,000)
Cash Flow from Financing Activities		
Proceeds from Issuance of Common Shares	30,000	
Bank Loan	120,000	
Dividends	(10,000)	
Change in Cash due to Financing Activities		140,000
Total Change in Cash		(2,300)
Opening Cash Balance		12,000
Cash at the end of the year		$9,700

Required

a) The company had a total decrease in cash during the year of $2,300. What is the primary cause of this decrease in cash?

---

b) Are there any concerns with operating activities?

Analysis

In a cash flow budgeting meeting, the company's CEO argued that, "we could have taken a larger bank loan to finance our land purchase in 2016. In fact, instead of borrowing only $120,000, we should have asked for $240,000. That would have put us into a better cash flow situation." Evaluate this comment from the CEO. How would a larger bank loan affect the cash flow of Dawson Corporation?

Case Study

CS-1 (❷)

Granite Surfaces specializes in making granite countertops. A new accounting clerk has compiled the following information to prepare the cash flow statement for the year ended December 31, 2016.

- Net income for the year was $114,140.
- Depreciation expense was $15,300.
- Equipment was sold for a gain of $16,000. Cash proceeds from the sale were $36,000.
- Equipment was purchased for $250,000.
- Dividends of $50,000 were paid.
- Accounts receivable increased by $31,400.
- Inventory decreased by $38,700.
- Accounts payable increased by $41,100.
- Bank loans increased by $55,000.
- Shares were sold for $50,000 (also their book value).
- Cash balance on January 1, 2016 was $114,800.
- Cash balance on December 31, 2016 was $117,640.

The cash flow statement the accounting clerk prepared is shown below.

Granite Surfaces Cash Flow Statement For the Year Ended December 31, 2016		
Cash Flow from Operating Activities		
Net Income	$114,140	
Add: Depreciation Expense	15,300	
Changes in Current Assets and Current Liabilities		
Increase in Accounts Receivable	31,400	
Decrease in Inventory	(38,700)	
Increase in Accounts Payable	41,100	
Sale of Equipment	36,000	
Purchase of Equipment	(250,000)	
Change in Cash due to Operating Activities		($50,760)
Cash Flow from Investing Activities		
Receipt of Bank Loan	55,000	
Change in Cash due to Investing Activities		55,000
Cash Flow from Financing Activities		
Payment of Cash Dividend	(50,000)	
Proceeds from Issuance of Common Shares	50,000	
Change in Cash due to Financing Activities		0
Net Increase (Decrease) in Cash		4,240
Cash at the Beginning of the Year		114,800
Cash at the End of the Year		$119,040

Required

a) Identify the problems with the cash flow statement that the accounting clerk prepared.

b) Prepare a corrected cash flow statement.

Chapter 11

FINANCIAL STATEMENT ANALYSIS

LEARNING OUTCOMES

❶ Explain the importance of analyzing financial statements

❷ Conduct horizontal and vertical analysis of financial statements

❸ Calculate and apply liquidity ratios

❹ Calculate and apply profitability ratios

❺ Calculate and apply operation management and leverage ratios

❻ Calculate and apply capital market ratios

❼ Identify the limitations of financial statement analysis

AMEENGAGE™ *Access **ameengage.com** for integrated resources including tutorials, practice exercises, the digital textbook and more.*

Assessment Questions

AS-1 (❶)

What is financial analysis?

_____

_____

_____

AS-2 (❹)

What is the formula for gross profit margin?

_____

_____

AS-3 (❹)

What does gross profit margin tell us?

_____

_____

_____

_____

_____

AS-4 (❹)

What does EBIT refer to?

_____

_____

_____

AS-5 (❺)

What is the formula for the interest coverage ratio?

_____

_____

_____

_____

AS-6 (❺)

Is it more preferable to have a higher or lower interest coverage ratio? Explain.

_____

_____

_____

_____

AS-7 (❹)

How do you calculate net profit margin?

_____

_____

_____

_____

AS-8 (④)

What is the formula for return on equity?

_____

_____

_____

_____

AS-9 (④)

For a particular company, if net income increased significantly from one year to the next, does this guarantee that the return on equity will also increase? Explain.

_____

_____

_____

_____

AS-10 (④)

What is the formula for return on assets?

_____

_____

_____

AS-11 (④)

What are some possible reasons why return on assets may have decreased from one period to the next?

_____

_____

_____

_____

AS-12 (❹)

Suppose that Company A and Company B generate the same level of net income each period. However, Company A is more capital-intensive than Company B. Which company will likely have the higher return on assets?

_____

_____

_____

_____

_____

AS-13 (❸)

What is the formula for the current ratio?

_____

_____

_____

AS-14 (❸)

What does the current ratio tell you?

_____

_____

_____

AS-15 (❸)

If current assets stay constant from one period to the next, but current liabilities increase, what will happen to the current ratio?

_____

_____

_____

_____

AS-16 (❸)

What is the formula for the quick ratio?

_____

_____

_____

AS-17 (❺)

What is the formula for debt-to-equity ratio?

_____

_____

_____

AS-18 (❺)

What is the formula for days-sales-outstanding?

_____

_____

_____

AS-19 (❺)

What does days-sales-outstanding tell you?

_____

_____

_____

AS-20 (❺)

How do you calculate accounts receivable turnover?

_____

_____

_____

_____

AS-21 (❺)

How is inventory days on hand calculated?

_____

_____

_____

AS-22 (❺)

What is the formula for the inventory turnover ratio?

_____

_____

_____

AS-23 (❼)

Why is it necessary to compare a company's calculated ratios with industry benchmarks?

_____

_____

_____

_____

_____

_____

_____

AS-24 (❹)

In the DuPont framework, return on equity is represented as a product of which three measurements?

_____

_____

_____

_____

AS-25 (❹)

What is the purpose of using the DuPont framework in examining a company's ROE from period to period?

_____

_____

_____

_____

_____

_____

AS-26 (❻)

How is book value per share calculated?

_____

_____

_____

_____

AS-27 (❻)

What does book value per share tell us?

_____

_____

_____

_____

_____

_____

_____

_____

AS-28 (❻)

How is earnings per share calculated? And what does it tell us?

_____

_____

_____

_____

_____

_____

_____

_____

_____

_____

AS-29 (❷)

How does the base-year differ from the base-figure?

_____

_____

_____

_____

_____

_____

_____

_____

_____

_____

_____

_____

Application Questions Group A

AP-1A (❹)

Simply Mullet Company reported the following.

- Sales: $1 million
- Cost of Goods Sold: $0.7 million
- Operating Expenses: $0.4 million
- Income Tax Rate: 20%

Calculate the gross profit margin. Differentiate between gross profit margin and gross profit.

_____

_____

_____

_____

_____

_____

_____

_____

_____

_____

_____

_____

_____

AP-2A (❹ ❺)

Trooper Nova Company reported the following.

Sales	$2.0 million
Cost of Goods Sold	0.7 million
Operating Expenses	0.4 million
Interest Expense included in Operating Expenses	0.05 million
Income Taxes	40% of income before tax
Shareholders' Equity (Average)	$20.0 million

Required

a) Calculate EBIT.

_____

_____

_____

_____

_____

_____

_____

b) Calculate the net profit margin.

_____

_____

_____

c) Calculate the interest coverage ratio.

_____

_____

_____

d) Calculate the return on equity. Banks are currently paying interest on deposits of 4% for money invested for two or more years. Comment on the ratio.

_____

_____

_____

_____

_____

_____

AP-3A (❸)

All-You-Can-Buy Company reports current assets of $6,572, and current liabilities of $2,786. Calculate the current ratio.

_____

_____

_____

AP-4A (❸)

Total current liabilities for Nicholson Restoration Company is $2,786. If cash is $2,000, short-term investments are $3,000, long-term investments are $1,000 and accounts receivable is $1,200, calculate the quick ratio.

_____

_____

_____

AP-5A (❹)

The income statement of Ellen Corporation for the years 2015 and 2016 showed the following gross profit.

	2016	2015
Sales Revenue	$97,200	$80,000
Cost of Goods Sold	72,000	50,000
Gross Profit	$25,200	$30,000

Required

a) Calculate the gross profit margins for both years.

_____

_____

_____

_____

_____

b) In which year does Ellen Corporation have a better gross profit margin? Explain.

_____

_____

_____

_____

_____

_____

_____

AP-6A (❺)

Kingston Company sells on credit, with the balance due in 30 days. The company's DSO ratio has changed from 60 days last year to 42 days this year. Are things getting better or worse? Explain the relationship between the sales terms and DSO.

_____

_____

_____

_____

_____

_____

_____

_____

_____

_____

_____

AP-7A (❹ ❺)

Presented below is the comparative income statement of Newton Company for 2016 and 2015.

Newton Company Income Statement For the Year Ended December 31, 2016		
	2016	**2015**
Sales	$194,890	$108,345
Cost of Goods Sold	116,934	65,007
Gross Profit	77,956	43,338
Operating Expenses		
Advertising Expense	4,000	2,000
Bank Charges Expense	580	0
Communication Expense	5,380	3,684
Legal and Professional Expense	6,000	3,950
Utilities Expense	3,330	1,503
Rent Expense	3,500	3,500
Repairs and Maintenance Expense	4,000	2,500
Salaries and Wages Expense	3,000	1,800
Transportation Expense	3,200	1,700
Interest Expense	1,248	580
Depreciation Expense	1,550	990
Total Operating Expenses	35,788	22,207
Operating Profit before Tax	42,168	21,131
Income Tax	12,650	6,339
Net Income	**$29,518**	**$14,792**

Required

a) Calculate the following ratios for both years.

- EBIT Percentage to Sales
- Interest Coverage Ratio

b) In which year does the company have a better performance with respect to the ratios calculated in part a)? Explain.

_____

_____

_____

_____

_____

_____

_____

_____

AP-8A (❺)

At the beginning of 2016, Acatela Corp. had inventory of $350,000. During the year, it purchased $220,000 worth of raw materials and sold $500,000 worth of inventory. Determine the inventory turnover ratio and the inventory days on hand ratio.

_____

_____

_____

_____

_____

_____

_____

_____

_____

_____

_____

_____

_____

_____

AP-9A (❺)

At the end of 2016, accounts receivable amounted to $200,000. At the beginning of the year, it was $165,000. Net credit sales for the year amounted to $813,000 and net income was calculated to be $229,000.

Determine the days sales outstanding ratio and the accounts receivable turnover ratio. Comment on the ability of the company to enforce its credit policy of 60 days.

_____

_____

_____

_____

_____

AP-10A (❸)

Selected financial data from Crew Company is provided below.

	As at December 31, 2016
Cash	$75,000
Accounts Receivable	$225,000
Merchandise Inventory	$270,000
Short-Term Investments	$40,000
Land and Building	$500,000
Current Portion of Non-Current Debt	$30,000
Accounts Payable	$120,000

Required

a) Calculate the quick ratio.

_____

_____

_____

_____

_____

b) What does Crew Company's quick ratio suggest about the company's performance?

_____

_____

_____

AP-11A (❺)

Bo Kyung Company had a debt-to-equity ratio last year of 1.46. This year, the ratio is 2.0. Are things getting better or worse? Explain your answer.

_____

_____

_____

_____

_____

AP-12A (❹ ❺)

Presented below are select figures from the balance sheet of Edison Company for 2016 and 2015.

Edison Company Balance Sheet As at August 31		
	2016	**2015**
Total Assets	$286,633	$203,311
Total Liabilities	119,006	69,873
Shareholders' Equity	167,627	133,438

In 2016, Edison Company had sales of $413,000 and net income of $46,500. Calculate the ratios for 2016 as indicated below.

    Return on Assets
    Asset Turnover
    Debt-to-Equity
    Debt-to-Assets

AP-13A (❻)

Testa Inc. had a net income of $158,000 for the year ended December 31, 2016. The company does not have any preferred shares and has 45,000 common shares outstanding for the entire year. During the year, they paid out $20,000 in dividends. Assume the market price of each common share is $24, which happens to be double of the book value per share.

Required

a)   Calculate earnings per share.

b)   Calculate the dividend payout ratio.

c)   Calculate the price earnings ratio.

AP-14A (❻)

Freebird Inc. had a net income of $358,400 for the year ended September 30, 2016. The company does not have any preferred shares and has 113,000 common shares outstanding for the entire year. During the year, they paid out $60,000 in dividends. Shareholders' equity is valued at $332,000.

Required

a) Calculate earnings per share.

_____

_____

_____

b) Calculate the dividend payout ratio.

_____

_____

_____

c) Calculate the price earnings ratio assuming the market price is $17 per share.

_____

_____

_____

d) Calculate the book value per common share.

_____

_____

_____

Analysis

Book value per share is rarely equal to the selling price of the share on the stock market. What are some factors that could cause the market value to differ from the book value?

_____

_____

_____

_____

_____

_____

AP-15A (❹)

Below is select financial statement information for Rock Co. and Roll Inc.

	Rock Co.	Roll Inc.
Sales	$348,500	$465,800
Cost of Goods Sold	106,293	160,701
Gross Profit	242,208	305,099
Expenses		
Operating Expense	52,275	69,870
Depreciation Expense	34,850	46,580
Advertising Expense	17,425	23,290
Interest Expense	15,683	37,264
Total Expenses	120,233	177,004
Net Income before Taxes	121,975	128,095
Income Tax Expense	62,730	83,844
Net Income	**$59,245**	**$44,251**
Cash	$14,850	$19,800
Accounts Receivable	25,000	22,500
Inventory	34,500	43,125
Equipment	85,800	81,510
Total Assets	**$160,150**	**$166,935**
Accounts Payable	$27,500	$24,750
Unearned Revenue	17,800	19,580
Long-Term Liabilities	29,350	62,925
Shareholders' Equity	85,500	59,680
Total Liabilities and Shareholders' Equity	**$160,150**	**$166,935**

Required

a) Calculate the profitability ratios shown in the table below.

	Rock Co.	Roll Inc.
Gross Profit Margin		
EBIT		
EBIT Percentage to Sales		
Net Profit Margin		
Return on Equity (ROE)		
Return on Assets (ROA)		

b) Based on the ratios from part a), which company would an investor be more likely to invest in?

AP-16A (❸ ❹ ❺)

Chicken Inc. and Egg Inc. are both in the toy retail business. All sales are on credit. Below is select financial information for the current year.

	Chicken Inc.	Egg Inc.
Income Statement		
Sales	$150,000	$135,000
Cost of Goods Sold	48,750	41,850
Gross Profit	101,250	93,150
Expenses		
Salaries Expense	22,500	27,000
Depreciation Expense	15,000	13,500
Advertising Expense	7,500	6,750
Interest Expense	6,750	5,130
Total Expenses	51,750	52,380
Net Income before Taxes	49,500	40,770
Income Tax Expense	26,250	24,300
Net Income	**$23,250**	**$16,470**
Balance Sheet		
Cash	$40,850	$24,510
Accounts Receivable	15,000	9,000
Inventory	34,500	20,125
Equipment	85,800	51,480
Total Assets	**$176,150**	**$105,115**
Accounts Payable	21,000	32,000
Unearned Revenue	27,800	18,670
Long-Term Liabilities	39,350	15,635
Shareholders' Equity	88,000	38,810
Total Liabilities and Shareholders' Equity	**$176,150**	**$105,115**

Required

a) Calculate each ratio listed below for each company and indicate which company is better for each one.

	Chicken Inc.	Egg Inc.	Which company is better?
Gross Profit Margin			
EBIT			
EBIT Percentage to Sales			
Net Profit Margin			
Return on Equity (ROE)			
Return on Assets (ROA)			
Asset Turnover			
Current Ratio			
Quick Ratio			
Debt-to-Equity Ratio			
Debt-to-Assets Ratio			
Days-Sales-Outstanding			
Accounts Receivable Turnover			
Inventory Days on Hand			
Inventory Turnover			

b) Examining all of the ratios, explain which company has a stronger financial position in regards to the following categories.

   i.   Profitability

_____

_____

_____

_____

_____

_____

   ii. Liquidity

_____

_____

_____

iii.   Managerial performance

_____

_____

_____

_____

_____

iv.   Leverage

_____

_____

_____

_____

AP-17A (❸ ❹ ❺)

The bookkeeper for Contigo Corporation has calculated several ratios for the past three fiscal years, shown below.

Required

a)   For each of the ratios, indicate whether the ratio is improving or weakening overall from the previous years.

Contigo Corporation				
Ratio	2016	2015	2014	Improving or Weakening?
Gross Profit Margin	32.80%	31.50%	31.10%	
EBIT Percentage to Sales	18.04%	17.33%	17.11%	
Interest Coverage Ratio	11.60	12.10	12.20	
Current Ratio	1.50	1.31	0.97	
Quick Ratio	0.90	0.79	0.73	
Debt-to-Equity Ratio	0.53	0.61	0.86	
Days-Sales-Outstanding	31.50	31.20	30.80	
Inventory Days on Hand	78.10	76.54	73.41	

b) Contigo is looking at applying for a new bank loan. The bank will examine the ratios that focus on the strength of Contigo's cash flow to determine if they should approve the loan. Based on the information in part a), would you recommend the bank to approve the bank loan? Why or why not?

_____

_____

_____

_____

_____

AP-18A (❷)

Perform a horizontal analysis for Groff Inc. Use 2013 as the base year and comment on the results.

Groff Inc. In Millions of Dollars				
	2016	**2015**	**2014**	**2013**
Revenue	500	400	300	200
Net Income	166	158	144	120

Groff Inc. In Millions of Dollars				
	2016	**2015**	**2014**	**2013**
Revenue				
Revenue Ratio				
Net Income				
Net Income Ratio				

_____

_____

_____

AP-19A (❷)

The following financial statements are taken from the records of Abaya Inc.

Abaya Inc. Balance Sheet As at December 31			
	2016	**2015**	**2014**
Current Assets			
Cash	$315,000	$325,000	$210,000
Accounts Receivable	140,000	198,000	92,000
Inventory	411,000	397,000	428,000
Short-Term Investments	115,000	100,000	100,000
Total Current Assets	981,000	1,020,000	830,000
Non-Current Assets	356,000	250,000	403,000
Total Assets	$1,337,000	$1,270,000	$1,233,000
Current Liabilties	214,000	265,000	90,000
Non-Current Liabilities	22,000	150,000	100,000
Total Liabilities	236,000	415,000	190,000
Shareholders' Equity	1,101,000	855,000	1,043,000
Total Liabilities and Shareholders' Equity	$1,337,000	$1,270,000	$1,233,000

Abaya Inc. Income Statement For the Year Ended December 31			
	2016	**2015**	**2014**
Sales	$701,000	$689,000	$514,000
Cost of Goods Sold	379,000	396,000	385,000
Gross Profit	322,000	293,000	129,000
Operating Expenses			
Advertising Expense	4,200	3,100	1,800
Bank Charges Expense	2,400	1,600	1,500
Communication Expense	5,600	3,700	4,300
Professional Fees Expense	11,800	5,400	6,800
Utilities Expense	8,600	7,580	5,250
Rent Expense	5,000	5,000	5,000
Repairs and Maintenance Expense	3,000	3,000	3,000
Salaries and Wages Expense	41,000	11,500	9,800
Transportation Expense	8,950	6,400	6,150
Interest Expense	18,600	12,600	8,500
Depreciation Expense	2,500	2,500	2,500
Total Expenses	111,650	62,380	54,600
Operating Profit before Tax	210,350	230,620	74,400
Income Tax	63,105	69,186	22,320
Net Income	$147,245	$161,434	$52,080

Required

a) Use the horizontal analysis techniques to compare the changes between the 2016 and 2015 balance sheet items.

Abaya Inc. Balance Sheet As at December 31, 2016				
	2016	**2015**	**$ Change**	**% Change**
Current Assets				
Cash	$315,000	$325,000		
Accounts Receivable	140,000	198,000		
Inventory	411,000	397,000		
Short-Term Investments	115,000	100,000		
Total Current Assets	981,000	1,020,000		
Non-Current Assets	356,000	250,000		
Total Assets	$1,337,000	$1,270,000		
Current Liabilities	214,000	265,000		
Non-Current Liabilities	22,000	150,000		
Total Liabilities	236,000	415,000		
Shareholders' Equity	1,101,000	855,000		
Total Liabilities and Shareholders' Equity	$1,337,000	$1,270,000		

b) Using 2014 as a base year, provide horizontal analysis of Sales, Gross Profit, Operating Expenses and Net Income.

	2016	**2015**	**2014**
Sales			
Gross Profit			
Operating Expenses			
Net Income			

c) Perform a vertical analysis of income statement for 2016, 2015 and 2014 and state all the income statement items as a percentage of net sales.

Abaya Inc. Income Statement For the Year Ended December 31, 2016			
	2016	**2015**	**2014**
Sales			
Cost of Goods Sold			
Gross Profit			
Operating Expenses			
Advertising Expense			
Bank Charges Expense			
Communication Expense			
Professional Fees Expense			
Utilities Expense			
Rent Expense			
Repairs and Maintenance Expense			
Salaries and Wages Expense			
Transportation Expense			
Interest Expense			
Depreciation Expense			
Total Expenses			
Operating Profit before Tax			
Income Tax			
Net Income			

AP-20A (❷)

Perform a vertical analysis (use Sales as the base) for Hiltonia Inc. Comment on the results. Note that figures are in millions of dollars.

	Hiltonia Inc.	
	2016	2015
Sales	$210	$250
COGS	150	200
Gross Profit	60	50
Selling Expenses	5	4
Wages	2	2
Rent	5	5
Total Expenses	12	11
Income before Tax	48	39
Taxes (35%)	16.8	13.65
Net Income	$31.2	$25.35

AP-21A (❸ ❹ ❺ ❻)

The income statements and balance sheets for Fallon Inc. are shown below for the last three fiscal years.

Fallon Inc. Income Statement For the Year Ended			
	2016	2015	2014
Sales	360,000	324,000	342,000
Cost of Goods Sold	108,000	89,100	85,500
Gross Profit	252,000	234,900	256,500
Expenses			
Operating Expense	54,000	48,600	51,300
Depreciation Expense	36,000	32,400	34,200
Advertising Expense	18,000	16,200	17,100
Interest Expense	6,800	7,650	8,500
Total Expenses	114,800	104,850	111,100
Net Income before Taxes	137,200	130,050	145,400
Income Tax Expense	72,000	64,800	68,400
Net Income	65,200	65,250	77,000

Fallon Inc. Balance Sheet At the Year Ended			
	2016	2015	2014
Cash	63,650	39,750	36,000
Short-Term Investments	11,000	10,000	8,000
Accounts Receivable	48,000	40,000	32,000
Inventory	18,000	22,500	27,000
Equipment	110,000	104,500	83,600
Total Assets	**250,650**	**216,750**	**186,600**
Accounts Payable	52,800	44,000	35,200
Current Portion of Long-Term Debt	8,500	8,500	8,500
Long-Term Debt	68,000	76,500	85,000
Common Shares	66,000	57,600	57,000
Retained Earnings	55,350	30,150	900
Total Liabilities and Shareholders' Equity	**250,650**	**216,750**	**186,600**

Other Information

1) Fallon Inc. has an unlimited number of shares authorized. The following number of common shares were outstanding in each year for the entire year: 2016—50,000, 2015—48,000, 2014—47,000.

2) The following dividends were paid: $40,000 in 2016, $36,000 in 2015 and $38,000 in 2014.

Required

a) Calculate the following ratios for Fallon Inc. for 2015 and 2016, and state whether the ratio improved or weakened in 2016.

	2016	2015	Improved or Weakened
Gross Profit Margin			
EBIT			
EBIT Percentage to Sales			
Interest Coverage Ratio			
Net Profit Margin			
Return on Equity (ROE)			
Return on Assets (ROA)			
Asset Turnover			
Current Ratio			
Quick Ratio			
Debt-to-Equity Ratio			
Debt-to-Assets Ratio			
Days Sales Outstanding			
Accounts Receivable Turnover			
Inventory Days on Hand			
Inventory Turnover			
Book Value per Share			
Dividend Payout Ratio			
Earnings per Share			

b) Fallon Inc. has a credit policy of 30 days. That is, it expects all customers to pay their bills within 30 days from sale. Comment on the company's ability to enforce this policy.

_____

_____

_____

_____

Analysis

Comment on the company's ability to cover its short-term debt obligations.

_____

_____

_____

_____

_____

AP-22A (❹)

Using the DuPont framework, calculate the missing item for each independent scenario.

i)

Net Profit Margin	10.30%
Asset Turnover Ratio	2.5
Equity Multiplier	2.3
ROE	?

ii)

Net Profit Margin	6.70%
Asset Turnover Ratio	?
Equity Multiplier	1.8
Net Income	$500,000
Beginning Shareholders' Equity	$800,000
Ending Shareholders' Equity	$1,300,000

iii)

Net Income	$200,000
Revenue	$600,000
Beginning Total Assets	$150,000
Ending Total Assets	$420,000
Equity Multiplier	?
ROE	35%

—————— **Application Questions Group B** ——————

AP-1B (❹)

Gross profit increased from $0.3 million in 2015, to $0.4 million in 2016. Gross profit margin decreased from 30% in 2015, to 28% in 2016. Comment on whether or not the company's profitability improved or deteriorated.

_____

_____

_____

_____

AP-2B (❹ ❺)

Sou Heng Company reported the following financial information at the end of 2016.

Sales	$2,110,000
Cost of Goods Sold	$740,000
Operating Expenses	$394,000
Interest Expense included in Operating Expenses	$53,000
Income Taxes	38% of income
Shareholders' Equity (Average)	$18,000,000

Required

a) Calculate EBIT.

_____

_____

_____

b) Calculate the net profit margin.

_____

_____

c) Calculate the interest coverage ratio.

d) Calculate the return on equity.

AP-3B (❸)

Goliath Gardening Services Ltd. reports current assets of $6,261, and current liabilities of $2,925. Calculate the current ratio. Comment on the company's ability to cover short-term obligations.

AP-4B (❸)

Selected financial data from Jai Home Company is provided below.

Cash	$85,000
Accounts Receivable	$233,000
Inventory	$267,000
Short-Term Investments	$50,000
Land and Building	$464,000
Current Portion of Non-Current Debt	$36,000
Accounts Payable	$117,000

Required

a) Calculate the quick ratio.

b) True or False? The quick ratio calculated in part a) shows that Jai Home Company is likely to meet its short-term cash obligations.

_____

_____

_____

_____

AP-5B (❹)

The income statement for Ellen Corporation for the years 2015 and 2016 showed the following information.

	2016	2015
Sales	$98,000	$66,000
Cost of Goods Sold	$77,000	$43,000
Gross Profit	$21,000	$23,000

Required

a) Calculate the gross profit margins for both years.

_____

_____

_____

_____

b) In which year does Ellen Corporation have a better gross profit margin?

_____

_____

_____

_____

_____

_____

_____

AP-6B (⑤)

At the end of 2016, accounts receivable for Genuine Interiors amounted to $210,000. At the beginning of the year, it was $200,000. Net credit sales for the year amounted to $900,000 and net income was calculated to be $205,000.

Determine the days sales outstanding ratio and the accounts receivable turnover ratio.

_____

_____

_____

_____

Analysis

Generally, a lower DSO is desirable, since it means collections are happening faster for the company. Is there any drawback to getting the DSO extremely low, such as to only two or three days?

_____

_____

_____

_____

_____

_____

_____

_____

_____

_____

_____

_____

_____

AP-7B (④ ⑤)

Presented below is the comparative income statement of JeansWear Company for 2016 and 2015.

JeansWear Company Income Statement For the Year Ended January 31		
	2016	**2015**
Sales	$184,794	$107,933
Cost of Goods Sold	115,550	69,022
Gross Profit	69,244	38,911
Operating Expenses		
Advertising Expense	3,040	1,490
Bank Charges Expense	556	24
Communication Expense	5,050	3,927
Legal and Professional Expense	5,540	3,010
Utilities Expense	3,074	1,754
Rent Expense	3,430	3,430
Repairs and Maintenance Expense	3,810	2,670
Salaries and Wages Expense	2,780	1,510
Transportation Expense	3,170	1,920
Interest Expense	1,343	579
Depreciation Expense	1,320	750
Total Operating Expenses	33,113	21,064
Operating Profit before Tax	36,131	17,847
Income Tax	10,839	5,354
Net Income	$25,292	$12,493

Required

a) Calculate the following ratios for both years.

	2016	2015
EBIT Percentage to Sales		
Interest Coverage Ratio		

b) In which year does the company have a better performance with respect to the EBIT Percentage to Sales calculated in part a)?

AP-8B (❺)

At the beginning of 2016, Percolate Corp. had inventory of $337,000. During the year, it purchased $210,000 worth of raw materials and sold $505,000 worth of inventory. Determine the inventory turnover ratio and the inventory days on hand ratio. Comment on the company's ability to sell its inventory, which has a shelf-life of 90 days.

_____

_____

_____

_____

_____

_____

AP-9B (❺ ❼)

Below is the past annual information for Java Time Inc. All sales are on credit.

	2016	2015	2014	2013
Sales	$44,500	$46,280	$47,900	$55,085
Sales Discounts	2,003	2,083	2,155	2,479
Net Sales	42,498	44,197	45,744	52,606
Accounts Receivable	6,130	5,885	5,649	5,084

Required

a) Calculate the following ratios for 2014, 2015 and 2016.

	2016	2015	2014
Days-Sales-Outstanding			
Accounts Receivable Turnover			

b) Are the ratios improving or weakening? What could the company do to better control these ratios?

_____

_____

_____

_____

_____

_____

_____

_____

Analysis

IFRS became the standard for public corporations in Canada in 2011. Before 2011, corporations followed Canadian GAAP for reporting. What is the implication of this if you were comparing a company's performance over several years, from 2009 to 2014?

_____

_____

_____

_____

_____

_____

_____

_____

_____

_____

_____

_____

AP-10B (❸)

Information from Silky Company's year-end financial statements is as follows.

	2016	2015
Current Assets	$200,000	$210,000
Current Liabilities	100,000	90,000
Shareholders' Equity	250,000	270,000
Net Sales	830,000	880,000
Cost of Goods Sold	620,000	640,000
Operating Income	50,000	55,000

Required

a) Calculate the current ratio for both years.

_____

_____

_____

_____

_____

_____

b) In which year does Silky Company have a better current ratio? Explain.

_____

_____

_____

_____

_____

_____

_____

_____

_____

AP-11B (❹)

Selected information for the Universal Company is as follows.

	December 31		
	2016	**2015**	**2014**
Common Shares	$840,000	$648,000	$550,000
Retained Earnings	370,000	248,000	150,000
Net Income for the Year	240,000	122,000	98,000

Required

a) Calculate the return on equity ratio for 2016 and 2015.

_____

_____

_____

_____

_____

b) Has the Universal Company's performance improved in 2016? Explain using the return on equity ratio.

_____

_____

_____

AP-12B (❺)

Below is selected financial information for Swingline Inc.

	2016	2015	2014	2013
Ending Inventory	4,850	5,626	5,723	6,014
Cost of Goods Sold	68,950	72,398	65,503	71,708

Required

a) Calculate the following ratios for 2016, 2015 and 2014.

	2016	2015	2014
Inventory Days-on-Hand			
Inventory Turnover			

b) Are the ratios improving or weakening? What could the company do to better control these ratios?

_____

_____

_____

_____

AP-13B (⑥)

Bluebird Inc. had a net income of $387,400 for the year ended August 31, 2016. The company does not have any preferred shares and has 125,000 common shares outstanding for the entire year. During the year, they paid out $60,000 in dividends.

Required

a) Calculate earnings per share.

_____

_____

_____

_____

b) Calculate the dividend payout ratio.

_____

_____

_____

_____

c) Calculate the price earnings ratio assuming the market price is $12 per share.

_____

_____

_____

_____

AP-14B (6)

Below is select financial statement information for Beta Corp. and Gamma Inc. in 2016.

	Beta Corp.	Gamma Inc.
Net Income	$157,840	$246,850
Shareholders' Equity		
Preferred Shares	$8,740	$74,055
Common Shares	102,596	160,453
Retained Earnings	7,352	4,355
Total Shareholders' Equity	$118,688	$238,863
Number of Common Shares Outstanding	10,820	12,400

Both Beta and Gamma declared preferred dividends in 2016. For Beta, the total preferred dividends were equal to 5% of net income; for Gamma, they were equal to 8% of net income.

Required

a) Calculate the following ratios for each company.

	Beta Corp.	Gamma Inc.
Book Value per Share		
Earnings per Share (EPS)		

b) Based on the ratios from part a), which company would an investor be more likely to invest in?

AP-15B (❸ ❹ ❺)

Below is select financial statement information for Alpha Inc. and Delta Corp.

	Alpha Inc.	Delta Corp.
Sales	$105,000	$87,000
Cost of Goods Sold	34,125	29,580
Gross Profit	70,875	57,420
Expenses		
Operating Expense	15,750	13,050
Depreciation Expense	10,500	8,700
Advertising Expense	5,250	4,350
Interest Expense	8,925	4,524
Total Expenses	40,425	30,624
Net Income before Taxes	30,450	26,796
Income Tax Expense	18,900	15,660
Net Income	**$11,550**	**$11,136**
Cash	$18,525	$24,700
Accounts Receivable	12,300	21,070
Inventory	34,500	30,125
Equipment	66,800	63,460
Total Assets	**$132,125**	**$139,355**
Accounts Payable	$43,530	$33,177
Unearned Revenue	17,800	29,580
Current Portion of Long-Term Debt	8,304	1,324
Long-Term Debt	27,680	8,825
Shareholders' Equity	34,811	66,449
Total Liabilities and Shareholders' Equity	**$132,125**	**$139,355**

Required

a) Calculate the liquidity and leverage ratios as shown in the table below.

	Alpha Inc.	Delta Corp.
EBIT		
Interest Coverage Ratio		
Current Ratio		
Quick Ratio		
Debt-to-Equity Ratio		

b) Which company has stronger liquidity and leverage ratios? Which company would a bank prefer to provide lending to based on the calculations in part a)?

_____

_____

_____

_____

_____

_____

_____

_____

_____

_____

_____

_____

_____

AP-16B (❼)

The following information is available for three different companies within the same industry.

	Company A	Company B	Company C
Cash	$7,800	$7,020	$10,530
Short-Term Investments	2,000	1,800	4,700
Accounts Receivable	8,250	7,425	13,138
Prepaid Assets	1,500	1,350	3,025
Inventory	9,500	8,550	5,825
Total Assets	$29,050	$26,145	$37,218
Accounts Payable	$4,300	$4,515	$4,730
Deferred Revenue	7,500	7,875	8,250
Current Portion of Long-Term Debt	15,800	16,590	17,380
Total Liabilities	$27,600	$28,980	$30,360

Required

a) Calculate the current and quick ratios for each company listed below. Which company has the strongest and weakest liquidity?

	Company A	Company B	Company C
Current Ratio			
Quick Ratio			

_____

_____

_____

b) Is the current ratio adequate for each company? Explain.

_____

_____

_____

_____

_____

c) Is the quick ratio adequate for each company? Explain.

_____

_____

_____

_____

_____

_____

_____

_____

Analysis

All three companies are public companies and thus prepare their financial statements in accordance to IFRS. Does this mean that all values on their financial statements can be compared without further investigation into how the values were calculated?

_____

_____

_____

_____

_____

_____

_____

_____

_____

_____

AP-17B (❸ ❹ ❺)

The most recent income statements and balance sheets for Midland Company are shown below.

Midland Company Income Statement For the Year Ended		
	2016	2015
Sales (on Credit)	$600,000	$540,000
Cost of Goods Sold	252,000	216,000
Gross Profit	348,000	324,000
Expenses		
Salaries Expense	210,000	162,000
Depreciation Expense	48,000	54,000
Advertising Expense	60,000	54,000
Interest Expense	9,000	9,000
Total Expenses	327,000	279,000
Net Income before Taxes	21,000	45,000
Income Tax Expense	8,400	18,000
Net Income	$12,600	$27,000

Midland Company Balance Sheet At the Year Ended		
	2016	2015
Cash	$76,540	$41,400
Accounts Receivable	37,000	44,400
Inventory	73,000	54,750
Equipment	110,000	158,000
Total Assets	**$296,540**	**$298,550**
Accounts Payable	$24,050	$28,860
Unearned Revenue	14,000	23,800
Long-Term Debt	60,000	60,000
Common Shares	50,000	50,000
Retained Earnings	148,490	135,890
Total Liabilities and Shareholders' Equity	**$296,540**	**$298,550**

Required

a) Calculate the following ratios for Midland Company for its 2016 fiscal year.

	Industry Average	Midland Company
Gross Profit Margin	40.0%	
Net Profit Margin	5.0%	
Return on Equity (ROE)	8.0%	
Return on Assets (ROA)	6.9%	
Quick Ratio	1.2	
Debt-to-Equity Ratio	0.75	
Days-Sales-Outstanding	40.0	
Inventory Turnover	6.1	

b) Perform some ratio analysis to determine how Midland Company has performed in 2016 compared to the industry average.

_____

_____

_____

_____

_____

AP-18B (❷)

Perform a horizontal analysis for Mazzic Inc. Use 2013 as the base year.

Mazzic Inc. In Millions of Dollars				
	2016	**2015**	**2014**	**2013**
Revenue	$469	$331	$292	$197
Revenue Percentage of 2013 Base-Year				
Net Income	$258	$223	$178	$84
Net Income Percentage of 2013 Base-Year				

AP-19B (❷)

The following financial statements are taken from the records of Jade Inc.

Required

a) Use the horizontal analysis techniques to compare the changes between 2016 and 2015 balance sheet items.

Jade Inc. Balance Sheet As at October 31				
	2016	**2015**	**$ Change**	**% Change**
Current Assets				
Cash	$318,300	$319,400		
Accounts Receivable	150,900	170,100		
Inventory	381,200	414,800		
Short-Term Investments	116,500	104,700		
Total Current Assets	966,900	1,009,000		
Non-Current Assets	527,850	318,900		
Total Assets	$1,494,750	$1,327,900		
Current Liabilities	$258,200	$224,600		
Non-Current Liabilities	126,900	109,500		
Total Liabilities	385,100	334,100		
Shareholders' Equity	1,109,650	993,800		
Total Liabilities and Equity	$1,494,750	$1,327,900		

b) Perform a vertical analysis of income statement for 2016 and state all the income statement items as a percentage of net sales.

Jade Inc. Income Statement For the Year Ended October 31		
	2016	**2016**
Sales	$700,800	
Cost of Goods Sold	373,800	
Gross Profit	327,000	
Operating Expenses		
Advertising	4,400	
Utilities	8,200	
Rent Expense	4,300	
Salaries and Wages	47,000	
Depreciation	34,530	
Interest	7,620	
Total Operating Expenses	106,050	
Operating Profit before Tax	220,950	
Income Tax	55,100	
Net Income	$165,850	

Analysis

Analyze the strengths and weaknesses of Jade's financial position based on the above horizontal and vertical analyses.

_____

_____

_____

_____

_____

_____

_____

_____

_____

_____

_____

_____

_____

AP-20B (❹ ❼)

The financial information at December 31, 2016 for two similar companies is shown below.

	Shaken Inc.		Stirred Inc.	
Balance Sheet				
Average Total Assets		$80,000		$50,000
Average Shareholders' Equity		30,000		45,000
Income Statement				
Sales		100,000		68,000
Cost of Goods Sold		40,000		34,000
Gross Profit		60,000		34,000
Operating Expenses				
Advertising Expense	$20,000		$5,000	
Salaries Expense	15,000		18,000	
Rent Expense	10,000		-	
Depreciation Expense	2,500		1,000	
Interest Expense	1,500		500	
Total Expenses		49,000		24,500
Net Income		$11,000		$9,500

Which company performed better during the year? Use relevant ratios to support your answer.

_____

_____

_____

_____

_____

_____

_____

_____

_____

_____

_____

_____

_____

_____

Analysis

The comparison between these two companies assumes they are following the same accounting standards (ASPE or IFRS). What impact, if any, would there be on the comparison if one followed ASPE and the other followed IFRS?

_____

_____

_____

_____

_____

_____

_____

_____

_____

_____

AP-21B (❸ ❹ ❺ ❻)

The income statements and balance sheets for Hathaway Inc. are shown below for the last three fiscal years. All sales are on credit.

Hathaway Inc. Income Statement For the Year Ended			
	2016	**2015**	**2014**
Sales	$800,000	$720,000	$760,000
Cost of Goods Sold	260,000	288,000	266,000
Gross Profit	540,000	432,000	494,000
Expenses			
Operating Expense	320,000	216,000	342,000
Depreciation Expense	64,000	72,000	76,000
Advertising Expense	80,000	72,000	114,000
Interest Expense	10,000	10,000	10,000
Total Expenses	474,000	370,000	542,000
Net Income (Loss) before Taxes	66,000	62,000	(48,000)
Income Tax Expense (Return)	29,700	27,900	(21,600)
Net Income (Loss)	$36,300	$34,100	($26,400)

Hathaway Inc. Balance Sheet At the Year Ended			
	2016	**2015**	**2014**
Cash	$234,400	$149,600	$80,000
Accounts Receivable	84,000	70,000	56,000
Inventory	136,000	102,000	61,200
Equipment	110,000	174,000	246,000
Total Assets	**$564,400**	**$495,600**	**$443,200**
Accounts Payable	$54,600	$45,500	$36,400
Unearned Revenue	21,000	23,100	18,900
Long-Term Debt	50,000	50,000	50,000
Common Shares	85,500	60,000	55,000
Retained Earnings	353,300	317,000	282,900
Total Liabilities and Shareholders' Equity	**$564,400**	**$495,600**	**$443,200**

Other Information

Hathaway Inc. has an unlimited number of shares authorized; the following common shares were outstanding in each year for the entire year: 2016—60,000, 2015—40,000, 2014—30,000.

Required

a) Calculate the following ratios for Hathaway Inc. for 2015 and 2016, and state whether the ratio improved or weakened in 2016.

	2016	2015	Improved or Weakened
Gross Profit Margin			
EBIT			
EBIT Percentage to Sales			
Interest Coverage Ratio			
Net Profit Margin			
Return on Equity (ROE)			
Return on Assets (ROA)			
Current Ratio			
Quick Ratio			
Debt-to-Equity Ratio			
Debt-to-Assets Ratio			
Days-Sales-Outstanding			
Accounts Receivable Turnover			
Inventory Days on Hand			
Inventory Turnover			
Book Value Per Share			
Earnings Per Share			

b) The owner of Hathaway Inc. is pleased to see that the company has started generating profits again and assumes that profitability must be improving. Perform some ratio analysis to determine if the owner's assumption is correct or not. Explain.

_____

_____

_____

_____

_____

Analysis

What does the company's inventory turnover ratio indicate/suggest?

_____

_____

_____

AP-22B (❹)

Du Inc. and Pont Manufacturer have been rival competitors in the hardware manufacturing for several years. The following data was compiled for 2016.

	Du	Pont
Net Profit Margin	15.00%	5.00%
Asset Turnover	0.42	1.24
Equity Multiplier	2.45	2.48

Required

a) Using the DuPont Framework, calculate the ROE for both companies.

_____

_____

_____

b) Compare the ROEs determined in part a). By analysing the three components of ROE in the DuPont Framework, explain and compare how both companies achieved their respective ROEs.

_____

_____

_____

_____

_____

_____

_____

Case Study

CS-1(❸ ❹ ❺)

Suppose that you have decided to invest some money in the stock market. After some research online, you come across the financial statements of Research in Motion. Before you can make a decision to invest in the company, you will need to calculate some key financial ratios and then analyze them. The statements are presented below.

Research in Motion Consolidated Balance Sheet (in thousands) As at February 29, 2016 and February 28, 2015		
	2016	**2015**
Assets		
Cash	$1,550,861	$835,546
Short-term Investments	360,614	682,666
Accounts Receivable	2,800,115	2,269,845
Inventory	621,611	682,400
Other Current Assets	479,455	371,129
Total Current Assets	**5,812,656**	**4,841,586**
Long-Term Investment	958,248	720,635
Property, Plant and Equipment	1,956,581	1,334,648
Intangible Assets	1,476,924	1,204,503
Total Assets	**$10,204,409**	**$8,101,372**
Liabilities		
Accounts Payable	$615,620	$448,339
Accrued Liabilities	1,638,260	1,238,602
Income Taxes Payable	95,650	361,460
Other Current Liabilities	82,247	66,950
Total Current Liabilities	**2,431,777**	**2,115,351**
Non-Current Liabilities	169,969	111,893
Total Liabilities	**2,601,746**	**2,227,244**
Shareholders' Equity		
Common Shares	2,113,146	2,208,235
Retained Earnings	5,489,517	3,665,893
Shareholders' Equity	**7,602,663**	**5,874,128**
Liabilities and Shareholders' Equity	**$10,204,409**	**$8,101,372**

**Research in Motion
Consolidated Income Statement (in thousands)
For the Year Ended February 29, 2016 and February 28, 2015**

	2016	2015
Revenue	$14,953,224	$11,065,186
Cost of Sales	8,368,958	5,967,888
Gross Profit	6,584,266	5,097,298
Operating expenses		
Research and Development	964,841	684,702
Selling, Marketing and Admin	1,907,398	1,495,697
Amortization Expense	310,357	194,803
Litigation Expense	163,800	0
Total Expenses	3,346,396	2,375,202
Operating Income Before Tax	3,237,870	2,722,096
Investment Income	28,640	78,267
Income Before Income Tax	3,266,510	2,800,363
Income Tax Expense	809,366	907,747
Net Income	$2,457,144	$1,892,616

**Research in Motion
Summary of the Cash Flow Statement (in thousands)
For the Year Ended February 29, 2016 and February 28, 2015**

	2016	2015
Net Cash Provided by Operations	$3,034,874	$1,451,845
Net Cash Used by Investing	($1,470,127)	($1,823,523)
Net Cash Used by Financing	($849,432)	$22,826
Net Increase (Decrease) in Cash	$715,315	($348,852)

Required

a) Calculate the following ratios for Research in Motion for 2016 and 2015. For any ratios that require an average (i.e. ROE), use the closing balance for the year.

	2016	2015
Gross Profit Margin		
Net Profit Margin		
Return on Equity		
Return on Assets		
Asset Turnover		
Current Ratio		
Quick Ratio		
Debt-to-Equity Ratio		

b) Based on the figures you calculated, has the company shown improvement in 2016 over 2015? Would you invest in Research in Motion? Explain.

_____

_____

_____

_____

_____

_____

_____

_____

_____

_____

_____

CS-2 (❸ ❹ ❺)

The following information has been taken from the financial statements of Ivory Inc.

Ivory Inc.	
Current Assets, December 31, 2016	$175,000
Total Assets, January 1, 2016	500,000
Total Assets, December 31, 2016	575,000
Current Liabilities, December 31, 2016	75,000
Total Liabilities, December 31, 2016	175,000
Shareholders' Equity, January 1, 2016	300,000
Shareholders' Equity, December 31, 2016	400,000
Net Sales	900,000
Depreciation Expense	10,000
Interest Expense	20,000
Income Tax Expense	25,000
Net Income	40,000

Required

a) Given the data for Ivory Inc., calculate the following ratios for 2016 (round to two decimal places). The company's ratios for 2015 are given for comparison.

	Ratio	2015
i)	Current Ratio	3.5
ii)	Interest Coverage Ratio	5.40
iii)	Debt to Equity	25.00%
iv)	Return on Assets	12.50%
v)	Return on Equity	20.20%
vi)	Net Profit Margin	8.60%

	Ratio	2016
i)		
ii)		
iii)		
iv)		
v)		
vi)		

b) Using 2015 as a comparison, discuss whether the company improved or deteriorated in its ability to (i) pay current liabilities as they come due, (ii) meet its non-current debt obligations and (iii) profitability. Be sure to make reference to specific ratios in your answers.

Critical Thinking

CT-1 (➐)

Financial statement analysis is performed on historical information. Since the past cannot be changed, calculating financial ratios is of no use. What management and investors are really interested in is the future, specifically the future profitability of a company. Discuss.

_____

_____

_____

_____

_____

_____

_____

_____

_____

_____

_____

_____

_____

_____

_____

_____

_____

_____

_____

_____